Sag Harbor Is

Sag Harbor Is

A Literary Celebration

Edited by Maryann Calendrille

Photographs by Kathryn Szoka

New York | Sag Harbor

Harbor Electronic Publishing

HEPDigital.com

2006

© 2006 Harbor Electronic Publishing
Library of Congress Control Number: 2006930086
ISBN 13: 978-1-932916-24-9 ISBN 10: 1-932916-24-5 (paper)
ISBN 13: 978-1-932916-25-6 ISBN 10: 1-932916-25-3 (eBook)

Printed in the United States of America.
Fourth Printing

CREDITS
Design and editing: Charles Monaco
Cover Design: Joseph Dunn
Cover photograph: John Steinbeck's writing studio, Kathryn Szoka

A NOTE ON THE TYPE

This book is set in Adobe Garamond. Based on the design of sixteenth-century typesetter Claude Garamond, the many Garamond faces have proved among the most durable and popular typefaces of the last 400 years. Adobe designer Robert Slimbach went to the Plantin–Moretus museum in Antwerp, Belgium, to study the original Garamond typefaces. These served as the basis for the design of the Adobe Garamond romans; the italics are based on types by Robert Granjon, a contemporary of Garamond's. This elegant, versatile design, especially suited to both screen and print, was the first Adobe Originals typeface, released in 1989. The display font is Baskerville.

To the memory and spirit of
William Mulvihill (1923–2004)

Writer, teacher, historian, environmentalist,
and champion of all that's best
about Sag Harbor

Sag Harbor Is

A Literary Celebration

Editor's Preface

With so many writers, editors, and poets packed into our tiny village, it's a wonder the clacking of typewriter keys didn't once drown out birdsong some early mornings. These days, those who make their living by the word, their computers humming, still lend the village its lettered reputation. If there's an air of nostalgia here it's because what's authentic about Sag Harbor seems as fleeting as spring; once you've noticed it, it's nearly gone. Sag Harbor still has a grocery store and a five-and-ten, but Main Street reads like a palimpsest of what once was. Anyone who can remember an earlier incarnation of a building on Main Street knows the place, feels a sense of pride about it. Many of the pieces included here call up the old ghosts and linger in their shadows offering several views of a village that has sparked the imagination of many.

From James Fenimore Cooper's *The Sea Lions* written in 1820, to Lorraine Dusky's recent tribute to the late Betty Friedan, we read of brave whalemen and of an irrepressible feminist. Walter Mosley's *The Man in My Basement* looks at the nature of good and evil; the avuncular voice in Bill Mulvihill's essay takes us back to a time when a ticket to *Gone with the Wind* cost forty cents, and a sailor's ghost laments a tragedy in Val Schaffner's "Whaler's Gift." Our poets linger at the shore lines, rather than tangle with the Saturday night crowds downtown.

The selections are serendipitous, rather than exhaustive. This volume does not include our many award-winning playwrights and children's book authors. Nor did we have space for the legions of fine journalists and magazine writers, though our village was home to Long Island's earliest newspaper. Sag Harbor's rich literary legacy deserves further investigation and another volume to come.

Many friends helped shape this collection. Thanks to Linda Francke and Canio Pavone for their expertise and advice; to Mary Ann Mulvihill, archivist of her father William Mulvihill's papers; to Robert Long, Martha Christina, and Tom Mathews for sound editorial counsel; to Carol T. Spencer for information about Ninevah; to Bill Pickens for information about Langston Hughes; to Sue Mullen and Suzan Smyth at the John Jermain Memorial Library; and to Alice Ragusa, archivist extraordinaire at *The East Hampton Star*. Each has contributed essential information. Dorothy Zaykowski's *Sag Harbor: The Story of an American Beauty* was an important source. We are grateful to Ted Conklin of The American Hotel, Dolores Zebrowski, and a generous anonymous donor for their support of the project.

Maryann Calendrille
Sag Harbor
2006

Introduction: Writing Sag Harbor

Mark Ciabattari

In the American classic *Moby Dick*, Herman Melville mentions Sag Harbor as being so wild it frightened the ship's harpooner, who stayed on board during a shore leave, content to remain a pagan if Christians acted as they did in a village where the local brothels and gin shops could swallow a sailor alive. Reaching back to its beginning in 1707 as the only village with a deep water port to calm the South Fork's inward bay, Sag Harbor has always been an exception to the prosperous farm villages of the Hamptons, sober havens founded by Puritans and exposed to the fierce Atlantic. As a bustling port town, Sag Harbor had no time for Puritans. Its noted Long Wharf extended Main Street out into the bay, opening the village to the greater world through its expansive sea trade. Nothing about Sag Harbor was provincial. Singularly it was a place for adventurous men and independent women. In whaling days, young farm lads came here to sign on to sail the world. The village's mothers became strong heads of family, their husbands far off in search of whales. Self-reliance, friendships, and mutual support grew amidst the village's women.

Sag Harbor's literary tradition ran to a love for narrative and poetry, sailors' tales of the deep, dark sea, together with a multi-cultural vision weaving the world into the village. John Steinbeck settled here in 1955 failing to find an East Coast sea town that had the feel of his Monterey, with its Cannery Row and colorful characters. He chanced upon this "out of the way" spot

and instantly fell in love. Sag Harbor was a real fishing village long linked to the sea. Characters peopled its curving Main Street and there were rough bars like the notorious Black Buoy, where John was soon a regular, plopping his mangy old poodle up on the bar.

Earthy local color was fine with Steinbeck. He wrote *The Winter of Our Discontent* set in a fictional Sag Harbor, and a best-selling travelogue, *Travels with Charley*, about a trip through the country in his pick-up truck with his dog. The first chapters were set in Sag Harbor. He was living in Sag Harbor when he won the 1962 Nobel Prize for Literature.

In the 1970s, critic Wilfrid Sheed was the literary nexus. Sheed and his writer wife Miriam Ungerer moved to a wonderful old home in the village and became a magnet for a literary crowd who came out from the city as summer renters and soon began to buy houses themselves. Sheed soon took charge of the weekly baseball game starring novelists and journalists, like Carl Bernstein of Watergate fame. Sheed called Sag Harbor the "Un-Hampton" — largely blue-collar (not the mega-wealth of the summer resort villages) and north of the Montauk Highway when the fashionable and chic were south of it. Alone of these South Fork villages, Sag Harbor had been a factory town. It also had an influx of new immigrants in the 1890s (establishing the first synagogue), and, as a major whaling port in pre-Civil War times, it harbored one of the country's first integrated industries, employing local freed blacks and native Montauketts, who lived in nearby Eastville. The one criterion for work on a whaler was great courage, regardless of skin color. A sense of tolerance grew here. Eastville and later Azurest became the summer resort areas of choice for prominent African–American judges, doctors, bankers, and authors. Langston Hughes, the poet of The Harlem Renaissance, visited in the 1950s. Olivia Ward Bush-Banks, descendant of African–Americans and Montauk natives, did pioneering multi-cultural work in the early 1900s. Gloria Naylor, author of *The Women of Brewster Street* was also a resident.

Early in the 1980s, former high school language teacher Canio Pavone founded his storefront bookshop, Canio's Books, with its iconic blue and white sign. Readings on Saturdays at six began then, the first by Nelson Algren. He had just taken up residence around the corner on Glover Street, across from the

house of Betty Friedan, author of *The Feminine Mystique*, the book that helped trigger the contemporary Women's Movement. Ironically, at the time, Algren had in his possession some 300 unpublished letters from his one-time lover, Simone de Beauvoir, Sartre's companion and author of *The Second Sex*, the first pre-Friedan discourse of the modern woman. Algren was buried in the village's Oakland Cemetery, first under a temporary marker that misspelled his name ("Nelson Algrin"), then under a gravestone with a Willa Cather quote — "The end is nothing, the road is all" — that distills what de Beauvoir thought of Americans like Algren who were true, living (not theoretical) existentialists.

The 1990s began the heyday of the Bay Street Theatre, co-founded by John Steinbeck's widow Elaine Steinbeck along with Emma Walton, Steve Hamilton, and Sybil Christopher. Bay Street produced plays by internationally recognized Sag Harbor playwrights Joe Pintauro and Lanford Wilson, as well as Terrence McNally and Edward Albee — the latter two former tutors of Steinbeck's sons. Form-breaking, post-modern historical novelist, E. L. Doctorow went on quietly building his life's work, its nostalgia aided by small-town village life, a five-and-dime on Main Street. In a studio over the old hardware store, Tom Harris fleshed out the cannibalistic Hannibal Lecter. Literary critic Morris Dickstein, from his summery cottage, re-established American classics for readers in the new century.

By 2000, Canio's was continuing its literary tradition under new owners Maryann Calendrille and Kathryn Szoka. Mr. Pavone's Canio's Editions, with over 20 titles by local authors on its list, had become a renowned small press. The Mark Twain-like monologist Spalding Gray came to the village to raise his family. In his book set here, *Morning, Noon and Night*, he rhapsodizes about the place in a way that can only seem tragic, given his later near-fatal car accident and ultimate suicide.

Canio's and its Saturday readings continue to form a thread through most all of this; walking through the door on any given day are some of the literary world's greats, Pulitzer and other prize winners; and in the future, no doubt will pass — the now unheard of writer whom America will hail as the new Fitzgerald, the new Flannery O'Connor.

from Sea Lions

James Fenimore Cooper

As a whaling town, Sag Harbor is the third or fourth port in the country and maintains something like that in rank in importance. A whaling haven is nothing without a whaling community. Without the last, it is almost hopeless to look for success. New York can, and has often fitted whalers for sea, having sought officers in the regular whaling ports; but it has been seldom that the enterprises have been rewarded with such returns as to induce a second voyage by the same parties.

It is as indispensable that a whaler should possess a certain *esprit de corps*, as that a regiment, or a ship of war, should be animated by its proper spirit. In the whaling communities, this spirit exists to an extent and in a degree that is wonderful, when one remembers the great expansion of this particular branch of trade within the last five-and-twenty years. It may be a little lessened of late, but at the time of which we are writing, or about the year 1820, there was scarcely an individual who followed this particular calling out of the port of Sag Harbor, whose general standing on board ship was not as well known to all the women and girls of the place, as it was to his shipmates. Success in taking the whale was a thing that made itself felt in every fibre of the prosperity of the town; and it was just as natural that the single-minded population of that part of Suffolk would regard the bold and skillful harpooner or lancer with favor, as it is for the bell at a watering place to bestow her smiles on one of the young heroes of Contreras or Cherubusco.

Customs House, Main Street

His particular merit, whether with the oar, lance, or harpoon, is bruited about, as well as the number of whales he may have succeeded in "making fast to," or those which he caused to "spout blood." It is true, that the great extension of the trade within the last twenty years, by drawing so many from a distance into its pursuits, has in a degree lessened this local interest and local knowledge of character; but at the time of which we are about to write, both were at their height, and Nantucket itself had not more of this "intelligence office" propensity, or more of the true whaling *esprit de corps,* than were to be found in the district of county that surrounded Sag Harbor.

Hannibal French house, Main Street

from **Moby Dick**

Herman Melville

Queequeg was a native of Kokovoko, an island far away to the West and South. It is not down in any map; true places never are.

When a new-hatched savage running wild about his native woodlands in a grass clout, followed by the nibbling goats, as if he were a green sapling; even then in Queequeg's ambitious soul, lurked a strong desire to see something more of Christendom than a specimen whaler or two. His father was a High Chief, a King; his uncle a High Priest; and on the maternal side he boasted aunts who were the wives of unconquerable warriors. There was excellent blood in his veins — royal stuff; though sadly vitiated, I fear, by the cannibal propensity he nourished in his untutored youth.

A Sag Harbor ship visited his father's bay, and Queequeg sought a passage to Christian lands. But the ship, having her full complement of seamen, spurned his suit; and not all the King his father's influence could prevail. But Queequeg vowed a vow. Alone in his canoe, he paddled off to a distant strait, which he knew the ship must pass through when she quitted the island. On one side was a coral reef; on the other a low tongue of land, covered with mangrove thickets that grew out into the water. Hiding his canoe, still afloat, among these thickets, with its prow seaward, he sat down in the stern, paddle low in hand; and when the ship was gliding by, like a flash he darted out; gained her side; with one backward dash of his foot capsized and sank his canoe; climbed up the chains; and throwing himself at full length upon the deck, grappled a ringbolt there, and swore not to let it go, though hacked in pieces.

In vain the captain threatened to throw him overboard; suspended a cutlass over his naked wrists; Queequeg was the son of a King, and Queequeg budged not. Struck by his desperate dauntlessness, and his wild desire to visit Christendom, the captain at last relented, and told him he might make himself at home. But this fine young savage — this sea Prince of Wales, never saw the captain's cabin. They put him down among the sailors, and made a whaleman of him. But like Czar Peter content to toil in the shipyards of foreign cities, Queequeg disdained no seeming ignominy, if thereby he might haply gain the power of enlightening his untutored countrymen. For at bottom — so he told me — he was actuated by a profound desire to learn among the Christians, the arts whereby to make his people still happier than they were; and more than that, still better than they were. But, alas! the practices of whalemen soon convinced him that even Christians could be both miserable and wicked; infinitely more so, than all his father's heathens. Arrived at last in old Sag Harbor; and seeing what the sailors did there; and then going on to Nantucket, and seeing how they spent their wages in *that* place also, poor Queequeg gave it up for lost. Thought he, it's a wicked world in all meridians; I'll die a pagan.

And thus an old idolator at heart, he yet lived among these Christians, wore their clothes, and tried to talk their gibberish. Hence the queer ways about him, though now some time from home.

By hints, I asked him whether he did not propose going back, and having a coronation; since he might now consider his father dead and gone, he being very old and feeble at the last accounts. He answered no, not yet; and added that he was fearful Christianity, or rather Christians, had unfitted him for ascending the pure and undefiled throne of thirty pagan Kings before him. But by and by, he said, he would return, — as soon as he felt himself baptized again. For the nonce, however, he proposed to sail about, and sow his wild oats in all four oceans. They had made a harpooneer of him, and that barbed iron was in lieu of a sceptre now.

I asked him what might be his immediate purpose, touching his future movements. He answered, to go to sea again, in his old vocation. Upon this, I told him that whaling was my own design, and informed him of my intention to sail out of Nantucket, as being the most promising port for an adventurous whaleman to embark from. He at once resolved to accompany me to that island, ship aboard the same vessel, get into the same watch, the same boat, the same mess with me, in short to share my every hap; with both my hands in his, boldly dip into the Potluck of both worlds. To all this I joyously assented; for besides the affection I now felt for Queequeg he was an experi-

Old Whalers' Church, Union Street

enced harpooneer, and as such, could not fail to be of great usefulness to one, who, like me, was wholly ignorant of the mysteries of whaling, though well acquainted with the sea, as known to merchant seamen.

His story being ended with his pipe's last dying puff, Queequeg embraced me, pressed his forehead against mine, and blowing out the light, we rolled over from each other, this way and that, and very soon were sleeping.

Selected Poems

Langston Hughes

from *The Collected Poems of Langston Hughes*

These poems pre-date Hughes' visit to Sag Harbor by some decades and were writ-
ten when he was sailing the west coast of Africa in the early 1920s, yet they cap-
ture what's universal about any port town, and, perhaps, illustrate some of the
reasons he was so fond of Sag Harbor. And since it was the friendships forged at
Lincoln University that eventually brought Hughes to Sag Harbor, we've
included his homage to that important institution. —Ed.

Sea Charm

Sea charm
The sea's own children
Do not understand.
They know
But that the sea is strong
Like God's hand.
They know
But that sea wind is sweet
Like God's breath,
And that the sea holds
A wide, deep death.

Water-Front Streets

The spring is not so beautiful there —
    But dream ships sail away
To where the spring is wondrous rare
    And life is gay.

The spring is not so beautiful there —
    But lads put out to sea
Who carry beauties in their hearts
    And dreams, like me.

Port Town

Hello, sailor boy,
In from the sea!
Hello, sailor,
Come with me!

Come on drink cognac.
Rather have wine?
Come here, I love you.
Come and be mine.

Lights, sailor boy,
Warm, white lights.
Solid land, kid.
Wild, white nights.

Come on, sailor,
Out o' the sea.
Let's go, sweetie!
Come with me.

Death of an Old Seaman

We buried him high on a windy hill,
But his soul went out to sea.
I know, for I heard, when all was still,
His sea-soul say to me:

Put no tombstone at my head,
For here I do not make my bed.
Strew no flowers on my grave,
I've gone back to the wind and wave.
Do not, do not weep for me,
For I am happy with my sea.

Lincoln University: 1954

This is the dream grown young
By but a hundred years,
The dream so bravely tended
Through a century of fears,
The dream so gently nourished
By a century of tears —
The dream grown ever younger,
Greener, fresher
Through the years of working,
Praying, striving, learning,
The dream become a beacon
Brightly burning.

Morning on Shinnecock

Olivia Ward Bush-Banks

from *The Collected Works of Olivia Ward Bush-Banks*

Her poetry uses the language of her times, a genteel vocabulary, an elegant style. Words were chosen for their cultured, aristocratic, parlor-acceptable, Victorian propriety. Yet she helped preserve her native culture and language particularly in her dramatic work Indian Trails: or Trail of the Montauk. *Her innate sensitivity to racial and social interaction is expressed in her work. She was proud of both her Native American heritage and her African–American lineage.*

—Elizabeth Thunder Bird Haile

The rising sun had crowned the hills,
  And added beauty to the plain;
O grand and wondrous spectacle!
  That only nature could explain.
I stood within a leafy grove,
  And gazed around in blissful awe;
The sky appeared one mass of blue,
  That seemed to spread from sea to shore.
Far as the human eye could see,
  Were stretched the fields of waving corn.
Soft on my ear the warbling birds
  Were herding the birth of morn.
While here and there a cottage quaint
  Seemed to repose in quiet ease
Amid the trees, whose leaflets waved
  And fluttered in the passing breeze.
O morning hour! so dear thy joy,

And how I longed for thee to last;
But e'en thy fading into day
Brought me an echo of the past.
'Twas this, how fair my life began;

How pleasant was its hour of dawn;
But, merging into sorrow's day,
Then beauty faded with the morn.

Drifting

Olivia Ward Bush-Banks

And now the sun in tinted splendor sank,
    The west was all aglow with crimson light;
The bay seemed like a sheet of burnished gold,
    Its waters glistened with such radiance bright.
At anchor lay the yachts with snow-white sails,
    Outlined against glowing, rose-hued sky.
No ripple stirred the waters' calm repose
    Save when a tiny craft sped lightly by.
Our host was drifting slowly, gently round,
    To rest secure till evening shadows fell;
No sound disturbed the stillness of the air,
    Save the soft chiming of the vesper bell.

Yes, drifting, drifting; and I thought that life,
  When nearing death, is like the sunset sky.
And death is but the slow, sure drifting in
  To rest far more securely, by and by.
Then let me drift along the Bay of Time,
  Till my last sun shall set in glowing light;
Let me cast anchor where no shadows fall,
  Forever moored within Heaven's harbor bright.

My Dear Long Island Home

Frances Hunt Palmer

The flat-lands, O the flat-lands
Of my dear Long Island home,
Where the sand shines white as silver,
And the waves dash high with foam;
Where the scrub-oak lines the pasture,
And the humble bumble-bee
Singing through the golden hour.
Calls to me:
    "Come, come; come home, come home."

The flat-lands, O the flat-lands
In October of the year,
When my soul is striving dumbly
With its tasks so drab and drear!
O, 'tis then I want my country,
And the stinging, ringing air,
Shouting through the scarlet tree-tops,
Calls me there:
    "Come, come; come home, come home."
It is there the sky's more blue;
It is there the sun's more golden;
And the clouds are always whiter,
And the lassie's hearts more true.
O, the flat-lands of my home-land
Is where I long to be,
And Nature's voice, insistent,
Calls to me
    "Come, come; come home, come home."

Sag Harbor: An American Beauty

Wilfrid Sheed

Much has changed in Sag Harbor since this piece was written. The village is pressed by fancy development projects bankrolled by big money. Remnants of Sheed's "un-Hampton" village are ever harder to find. —Ed.

"The un-Hampton" is what it calls itself, and that's one way of looking at it. If ever a place could be opulently defined by what it isn't, the place is Sag Harbor. When its famous neighbors, East, South and Bridge Hamptons, were still a God-fearing paradise of farms and fish, Sag Harbor proposed itself as sin city, the libido of the South Fork, full of foreigners and mischief and whale oil, the fool's gold of the 1820s and 1830s; but when the neighbors began to take in rich boarders, and acquire the sheen of a vast real estate ad, Sag Harbor resurfaced as the industrial north or blue-collar Hampton, triumphantly the wrong side of the tracks.

And even today, when all the Hamptons, both real and un-, are obliged to depend on outside visitors rather more than they care to, the local styles remain as different as Laurel and Hardy, yin and yang: bearing out the historical principle that no area is too small (we're talking here of four miles at the nearest, ten at the farthest) to generate total opposites.

That, as I say, is one way to look at it. But Sag Harbor has always had more important fish to fry than worrying about the damn Hamptons. Thanks to a relatively peaceful history, America is blessed with an unusual

---

33

number of historical sites in which nothing much happened (one civil war is barely enough to go round, by European standards), and day-trippers to the South Fork sometimes seem politely puzzled as to just what it is they're supposed to look at around here....

Picture, if you will, a whaleboat sailing right up to the foot of Main Street — and this could be any day of the week or month of the year — loaded with several fortunes and God knows how many great stories, while at the next dock another hopeful is being outfitted with ten tons of bully beef for the captain alone, and all the hardtack they can eat for whatever rogues and dreamers, slaves and novelists (Melville was here), Queequegs and Ishmaels, the company has managed to con or dragoon into serving under him.

It's a small town, twenty-five hundred tops, but the number is forever being augmented by passing Fijians, Sandwich Islanders, and whatever else the wind has blown in — a far cry from today's summer people with their designer clothes and hurry-up suntans. Along the shore, shipwrights and sailmakers and other boat-minded people work, it's fair to suppose, with the special zest one gets from being part of a great enterprise: Unlike most twentieth-century workers, they have only to look out the door to see the flourishing fruit of their labors. It is, in short, a town with a purpose in life, and it always has something to look forward to. And make me a better offer than that.

All this is the patrimony of the Sag Harborite every time he looks out the door, and the reason he has it is that this is still recognizably the same town it always was, with all the inevitable changes somehow working in the right direction. A politician might call this effect the Miracle of Sag Harbor and he might be right; but it had nothing to do with politicians or with any human intention whatever. But at this point, we have to start over — and forget for a moment you ever heard of the Hamptons....

Until recently Sag Harbor has made it almost entirely on luck. The town came into money at a very good time — the first half of the nineteenth century — and ran out (and stayed out) of it at a good time too: ever since. In the 1830s and 1840s, when Sag Harbor was a booming whale town, you

Bulova Watchcase Factory

didn't need good taste to build well — it took genius not to. And by the time ugliness had entered America, Sag Harbor couldn't afford it.

In between, and before and since, Sag Harbor has been visited by a host of withering fires that would have gutted the charm out of a less favored community, but have only served to prune it, while sparing, to our eyes at least, just the right amount, like a biblical plague that knows precisely what it's doing. (The fires also left us with undoubtedly the world's finest volunteer fire department and what might be called a fire department culture: The firemen and the houses they operate from are simply the cream and quintessence of Sag Harbor, as I learned with joy the night my chimney almost burned down.)

Sag Harbor's Golden Age of whaling was over in a blink; a gaudy, vivid dream of no more than thirty years or so that stamped the town forever. Up until the end of the eighteenth century, whales had frisked along the coast and just about come on shore, so hunting them was no big deal: Indians and white men practically took turns at it — the whites for cash, and the Indians for worship (and what could be better to worship than whales?). But by 1817, when Sag Harbor's first deep-sea expedition was launched, the whales had gotten the hint, and there ensued one of the great cat-and-mouse hunts in history, ennobled perhaps by our greatest novel: Sag Harbor thinks so anyway, and every summer, residents combine to read *Moby Dick* out loud and right through at Canio's rare-book store.

The game reached a fever peak in 1847, Sag Harbor's greatest year; and then the fever broke and the whole thing was over, just two years later. Unlike New Bedford, Sag Harbor had no hinterland to speak of; it was a great port attached to nothing much. So when the first batch of adventurers sailed for California to track down the Great Gold Whale, there was no one left to replace them. Local capital was still tied up paying for the latest fire — the 1845 edition was a beaut — and besides, petroleum was moving up fast on sperm oil in the market, and the rest you know.

Ever since, Sag Harbor has been playing catch-up history. The American landscape is strewn with towns that have been seduced, and abandoned like trash cans in the wake of our latest whale, but Sag Harbor might be described as a ghost town that wouldn't lie down. From the Civil War onward, successive enterprises have started up with a high heart, only to burn down or otherwise fail, until God's greatest gift to mankind, the humble watchcase, arrived to stay in 1881.

Joseph Fahys's watchcase factory, which was later purchased and run by the Bulova Company, is the symbolic building of Sag Harbor's never-ending effort to get back on its feet. A gorgeous specimen of Gradgrind architecture, the factory now stands out from its gentle neighbors as stately as the Eiffel Tower in Paris, or Keble College, Oxford, one of those epic anomalies that help to define a landscape by clashing with it.

The Bulova building also represents a prickly, permanent-outsider strain in the local psyche that also clashes slightly with the landscape and saves us from any temptation to prettify or sentimentalize our surroundings. Like a WPA mural in the 1930s, the factory reminds one that, no matter how charming or instructive other people may happen to find it at the moment, Sag Harbor always goes on about its business as if bad times were just around the corner. Unlike other famous beauties, it has neither the time nor the inclination to preen or rest on its laurels — if anything, quite the contrary. "I'm fed up with being quaint," said a candidate for trustee not so long ago, meaning, I presume, "I'm fed up with being stared at." And the chip on her

Marty Trunzo's barbershop, Main Street

shoulder goes back a long way and is very much part of our living history.

When Mr. Fahys opened his factory, and later when Grumman Aircraft opened another one, which is now utterly deceased, the Poles and Germans and Italians who showed up for work there had no reason to be interested in whaling history, or in the great houses and great families that celebrated it. The families sure as hell weren't interested in them. If a visitor today gets the feeling that some old-timers are not totally glad to see him, he can rest assured his welcome is warmer than theirs or their grandparents' ever was. In fact, he is part of a great tradition. Sag Harbor has been going to the dogs for a long time now, and the visitor is just the latest evidence of it.

The Sag Harbor response to this ever-miserable state of affairs is creative grumbling, our secret language: You can fit in anywhere if you know how to grumble wittily enough. But in truth, all those infusions of new, unwanted blood seem to have given Sag Harbor a jump and an edge that the other towns out here lack. Driving home from Southampton on a winter evening last year when all the stores there had closed, I found Sag Harbor still humming and brimming with life, and I thought, "This is the live one"; the others will have to wait till spring.

Contributing to — or at least, not detracting from — this full-calendar vitality is a growing corps of "year-round summer people," as they're called, who weekend out here and actually use the village as opposed to just hiding in their houses and sending out for food. When a newcomer approaches a Hampton with his wallet out, local beauty lovers tremble and zoning boards brace themselves until they know exactly what the fellow has in mind. But most of the new settlers to Sag Harbor get the point right away: They came here because they like it exactly as it is, and will fight anyone, even the locals themselves to keep it that way.

This, of course, reverses the classic picture of marauding Manhattanites and bestial developers riding roughshod over local sensibilities. If anything the tensions ran the other way. To a no-nonsense Sag Harborite, the late arrivals must have seemed no better than a pack of precious, independently wealthy antiquarians bent on keeping them from expanding their businesses and creating jobs and living like the rest of America: hence the "quaintness" charge....

Writers have proved particularly partial to this style, but only such writers as share some of it already. Our first big name, if one excepts the transient Fenimore Cooper, was John Steinbeck, the chronicler of Okies and paisans and the roustabouts of Cannery Row: Sag Harbor suited him to a T. (When Steinbeck won the Nobel Prize for literature, legend has it that local residents polled about it knew him mostly for his boat, which he kept admirably clean and shipshape. First things first in Sag Harbor, and water is both our history and our esthetic.)

Our current writers in residence include Lanford Wilson, E. L. Doctorow, and Thomas Harris, and I'll say no more about them: No writer ever came to Sag Harbor in search of more attention. But it might be taken as a general principle that if you see someone in particularly shabby work clothes — and I don't mean designer work clothes, either — it just might be a writer, and not neces-

Bess Daniels, Peggy Schwenk, and Dolores Zebrowski, Memorial Day parade

sarily a famous one. Sag Harbor actually contains some writers who haven't made it yet, as well as a number of no-name or some-name journalists who probably enjoy the intricacies of small-town gossip as much as anything.

"Did you see what they've done to the old Bagbalm house?" "I hear the lady who just moved in was the mistress of Calvin Coolidge." The houses are like characters in a long-running play that the whole town is invited to watch, and tell stories about forever — a hard offer for a writer to refuse.

Sag Harbor had to wait a lot longer than Charleston for its historical society: In fact, a preservationist might have despaired of its ever getting here at all. But it got here all right, and it's not just a Manhattan Project either, but a properly homegrown association of new and old Sag Harborites who love the town to about equal distraction. Largely thanks to its good work, the robust heart of Sag Harbor is now safe, both from outsiders and from itself.

If one compares it with some of the museum-towns one has known, a case can be made that this vibrant, idiosyncratic little town is all the better for the wait.

My War with the Ospreys

John Steinbeck

My war with the ospreys, like most ones, was largely accidental and had a tendency to spread in unforeseen directions. It is not over yet. The coming of winter carried an uneasy truce. I had to go into New York while the ospreys migrated to wherever they go in the winter. Spring may open new hostilities, although I can find it in my heart to wish for peace and even friendship. I hope the ospreys, wherever they may be, will read this.

I shall go back to the beginning and set down my side of the affair, trying to be as fair as I possibly can, placing Truth above either propaganda or self-justification. I am confident that until near the end of the association my motives were kind to the point of being sloppy.

Two years and a half ago I bought a little place near Sag Harbor, which is quite near to the tip of Long Island. The outer end of Long Island is like the open jaws of an alligator and, deep in the mouth, about where the soft palate would be, is Sag Harbor, a wonderful village inhabited by people who have been here for a long time. It is a fishing town, a local town which has resisted the inroads of tourists by building no motor courts and putting up no hotels.

Sag Harbor was once one of the two great whaling ports of the world and was, according to local accounts, not at all second to Nantucket Island. At that time no fewer than one hundred and fifty whaling bottoms roved the great seas and brought back their riches in oil. Sag Harbor and Nantucket lighted the lamps of the world until kerosene was developed and the whaling industry languished.

With the wealth brought back by the whalers, beautiful houses were built in the village during the early 1800s, houses of neo-Greek architecture with fluted columns, Greek key decorations, with fanlights and Adam doors and mantels. Some of these magnificent old houses have widow's walks, those high balconies on which the women kept watch for the return of their men from their year-long voyages. Some of these old houses are being rediscovered and restored. Many of the streets of Sag Harbor are named after old whaling men. My own place is near Jesse Halsey Lane and he is still locally known as Old Cap'n Jesse. I have a picture of his rough and whiskered face.

The place I bought is not one of the great old houses but a beautiful little point of land on the inland waters, a place called Bluff Point, with its own little bay — incidentally a bay which is considered hurricane-proof. Ordinarily only two boats are moored there, mine and one other, but during hurricane warnings as many as thirty craft come in for anchorage until the all-clear is broadcast.

My point, just under two acres, is shaded by great oak trees of four varieties and there are many bushes and pines to edge it on the water side. I myself have planted a thousand Japanese black pines, furnished by the State of New York to edge my point, to hold the soil with their roots and eventually to curve beautifully inward, urged by the wind which blows every day of the year — sometimes a zephyr and sometimes a fierce and strident gale.

Greensward grows on my place. On the highest point I have a small, snug cottage and in front of it a pier going out to nine feet at low water so that a fairly large boat can dock. My own boat, the *Lillymaid*, with Astolat as her port of registry, is named for my wife. She, the boat, is a utility craft twenty feet long, a clinker-built Jersey sea skiff. Her eight-foot beam makes her highly dependable and seaworthy. Many of these specifications could also describe my wife. She is not clinker-built, however. The *Lillymaid* has a Navy top to put up when the weather gets too rough and she has a hundred-horsepower engine so that we can run for it if a storm approaches. She is a lovely, efficient and seaworthy craft and all we need for the fishing and coastal exploring which is our pleasure.

Our house, while very small, is double-walled and winterized so that we can drive out during cold weather when the not-so-quiet desperation of New York gets us down.

My young sons, ten and twelve, but eight and ten when the osprey war began, adore the place and spend most of their summers here, exploring about in their skiffs or quarreling happily on the pier or on the lawn under the oak trees. My wife, who I believe was realistically skeptical when I bought the place, has become its staunchest defender.

Our association with the village people of Sag Harbor is, I think, pleasant to all of us. I come originally from a small town on the West Coast, a fishing town where my people have lived for a long time. And I find that what applies in my home country is equally acceptable in Sag Harbor. If you pay your bills, trade locally as much as possible, mind your own business and act reasonably pleasant, pretty soon they forget that you are an outlander. I feel that I belong in Sag Harbor and I truly believe that the people of the village have accepted us as citizens. I do not sense the resentment from them which is reserved for tourists and summer people.

But I must get back to the ospreys, because with them I have not only failed to make friends but have, on the contrary, been insulted, have thrown down the gauntlet and had it accepted.

On the West Coast, in California's Monterey County where I was born, I learned from childhood the grasses and flowers, the insects and the fishes, the animals from gopher and ground squirrel to bobcat and coyote, deer and mountain lion, and of course the birds, the common ones at least. These are things a child absorbs as he is growing up.

When I first came to Long Island I knew none of these things. Trees, grasses, animals and birds were all strange to me; they had to be learned. And sometimes the natives could not help me much because they knew the things so well and deeply that they could not bring them to the surface.

Thus with books and by asking questions I have begun to learn the names of trees and bushes, of berries and flowers. With a telescope, a birthday present from my wife, I have watched muskrats and a pair of otters swimming in our bay. I have tried to identify the migrating ducks and geese when they sit down in our bay to rest from their journey.

The mallards mate and nest in the reeds along our waterline and bring their ducklings for the bread we throw to them from the pier. I have watched my boys sitting quietly on the lawn with the wild ducks crawling over their legs to get pieces of doughnut from their fingers.

The baby rabbits skitter through my vegetable garden and, since I like the rabbits better than my scrawny vegetables, I permit them not only to live but to pursue happiness on my land.

Our house has a glassed-in sun porch and outside its windows I have built a feeding station for birds. Sitting inside I do my best to identify the different visitors with the help of an Audubon and I have not always, I confess, been successful. There is one common blackish bird which looks to be of the grackle persuasion but his bill is the wrong color and I don't know what he is.

In the upper branches of a half-dead oak tree on the very tip of our point, there was, when I took possession, a tattered lump of trash which looked like

an unmade bed in a motor court. In my first early spring a native named Ray Bassenden, our contractor and builder, told me, "That's an osprey's nest. They come back every year. I remember that nest since I was a little boy."

"They build a messy nest," I said.

"Messy, yes," he said professionally, "but I doubt if I could design something the winds wouldn't blow out. It isn't poetry but it's darned good architecture from a staying point of view."

Toward the end of May, to my delight, the ospreys came back from wherever they had been, and from the beginning they fascinated me. They are about the best fishermen in the world and I am about the worst. I watched them by the hour. They would coast along hanging on the breeze perhaps fifty feet above the water, then suddenly their wings raised like the fins of a bomb and they arrowed down and nearly always came up with a fish. Then they would turn the fish in their talons so that its head was into the wind and fly to some high dead branch to eat their catch. I became a habitual osprey watcher.

In time, two of my ospreys were nudged by love and began to install new equipment in the great nest on my point. They brought unusual material — pieces of wood, rake handles, strips of cloth, reeds, swatches of seaweed. One of them, so help me, brought a piece of two-by-four pine three feet long to put into the structure. They weren't very careful builders. The ground under the tree was strewn with the excess stuff that fell out.

I mounted my telescope permanently on the sunporch and even trimmed some branches from intervening trees, and from then on, those love-driven ospreys didn't have a moment of privacy.

Then June came and school was out and my boys trooped happily out to Sag Harbor. I warned them not to go too near the point for fear of offending the nest builders, and they promised they would not.

And then one morning the ospreys were gone and the nest abandoned. When it became apparent that they weren't coming back I walked out to the point and saw, sticking halfway out of the nest, the shaft and feathers of an arrow.

Now Catbird, my youngest son, is the archer of the family. I ran him down and gave him what for in spite of his plaintive protests that he had not shot at the nest.

For a week I waited for the birds to come back, but they did not. They were across the bay. I could see them through the telescope building an uneasy nest on top of a transformer on a telephone pole where they were definitely not wanted.

I got a ladder and climbed up to the nest on our point and when I came down I apologized to Catbird for my unjust suspicions. For in the nest I had found not only the arrow, but my bamboo garden rake, three T-shirts belonging to my boys and a Plaza Hotel bath towel. Apparently nothing was too unusual for the ospreys to steal for their nest building. But our birds were definitely gone and showed no intention of returning. I went back to my Audubon and it told me the following:

"Osprey (fish hawk) *Pandion haliaetus*, length 23 inches, wingspread about 6 ½ feet, weight 3 ½ pounds.

Steinbeck's studio at Bluff Point

"Identification — in flight the wings appear long and the outer half has a characteristic backward sweep.

"Habits — (age 21 years) Provided they are not molested, ospreys will nest wherever there is a reasonably extensive body of clear water and some sort of elevated nest sites exist. The birds have little fear of man and are excellent watchdogs, cheeping loudly at intruders and driving off crows and other birds of prey. For this reason platforms on tall poles are often erected to encourage them to nest about homes and farmyards. Their food consists entirely of fish. These they spot from heights of thirty to one hundred feet, then, after hovering for a moment, they half close their wings and plunge into the water. The fish is seized in their talons, the toes of which are used in pairs, two to a side. This and the rough surface of the foot gives them a firm grip on the most slippery prey. After a catch, they rise quickly... and arrange the fish head first."

There followed a list of the kinds of fish they eat and their range and habits. Those were our boys, all right.

I must admit I had been pleased and a little proud to have my own osprey nest, apart from being able to watch them fish. I had planned to observe the nestlings when they arrived. The empty nest on the point was a matter of sorrow and perplexity to me. The summer was a little darkened by the empty nest, and later the winter winds ripped at its half-completed messiness.

It was in February of 1956 that the answer came to me. If people put up platforms on poles, why could I not build a nest so attractive as to be irresistible to any passing osprey with procreation on his mind? Why could I not win back my own birds from the uncomfortable nest which the power company had meanwhile torn off the transformer? I had been to Denmark and had seen what the country people there did for storks. And the storks loved them for it and had their young on the rooftops and year by year brought luck to their benefactors.

In the late winter I went to work. Climbing the oak tree on the point, I cleaned away the old debris of the nest. Then I mounted and firmly wired in place horizontally a large wagon wheel. I cut dry pampas grass stalks and bound them in long faggots. Then with the freezing blasts of winter tearing at my clothes, I reascended the tree and wove the reeds into the spokes of the wheel until I had a nest which, if I had any oviparous impulses, I should have found irresistible.

My wife, dressed in warm clothing, stood dutifully on the ground under the trees and hooked bundles of reeds on the line I threw down to her. She has a highly developed satiric sense which on other occasions I have found charming. She shouted up against the howling wind: "If anybody sees you, a middle-aged man, up a tree in midwinter, building a nest, I will have trouble explaining it to a sanity commission."

Misplaced humor can, under some circumstances, almost amount to bad taste. Silently and doggedly I completed what I believe was the handsomest nest in the Western Hemisphere. Then I went back to my sunporch to await eventualities.

I did have some difficulty explaining the project to my boys. To my oldest son Thom's question "Why do you build nests for birds?" I could only jocularly reply, "Well, I can build a better nest than they can, but I can't lay eggs, so you see we have to get together."

The winter was long and cold and there was hardly any spring at all. Summer came without warning about June 1. I had trouble with the novel I was writing since I had to rush constantly to the telescope to see whether the ospreys, my prospective tenants, had returned.

Then school was out and my boys moved to Sag Harbor and I put them on watch.

One morning Catbird charged into my study, which is a corner of the garage.

"Ospreys!" he shouted, "Come running — ospreys!"

"Sh!" I shouted back. "Keep your voice down. You'll disturb them."

I rushed for my telescope, bowling Catbird over in my rush and tripping over Thom's feet.

There were the ospreys all right. But they weren't settling into my beautiful nest. They were dismantling it, tearing it to pieces, lifting out the carefully bound reed pads and carrying them across the bay and propping them clumsily on top of the same transformer.

Of course my feelings were hurt. Why should I deny it? And on top of all my work. But on the heels of injury came anger. Those lousy, slipshod, larcenous birds, those ingrates, those — those ospreys. My eyes strayed to the shotgun that hangs over my fireplace, but before I could reach for it a Machiavellian thought came to me.

I wanted to hurt the ospreys, yes. I wanted revenge on them, but with number-four shot? No. I ached to hurt them as they had hurt me in their feelings — psychologically.

I am an adept at psychological warfare. I know well how to sink the knife into sensibilities. I was coldly quiet, even deadly in my approach and manner, so that my boys walked about under a cloud and Thom asked, "What's the matter, Father, did you lose some money playing poker?"

"You stay out of the garage," I said quietly.

I had made my plan. I declared the garage off limits to everyone. My novel came to a dead stop. Daily I worked in the garage using pieces of chicken wire and a great deal of plaster of Paris.

Then I paid a call on my neighbor, Jack Ramsey, a very good painter, and asked him to come to my workshop. And to bring his palette and brushes. At the end of two days we emerged with our product — a life-size perfect replica of a nesting whooping crane. It is my belief that there are only thirty-seven of these rare and wonderful birds in the world. Well, this was the thirty-eighth.

Chuckling evilly I hoisted the plaster bird up in the tree and wired her firmly in the nest where her blinding white body, black tail and brilliant red mask stood out magnificently against the sky. I had even made her bill a little overlarge to take care of foreshortening.

Finally I went back to the sun porch and turned my telescope on the ospreys, who pretended to go about their nest building on the transformer as though nothing had happened. But I knew what must be going on over there, although they kept up their façade of listlessness, and I must say they were building an even messier nest than usual.

Mrs. Osprey was saying, "Lord almighty. George! Look who has moved into the apartment *you* didn't want. Why did I listen to you?"

To which he was replying, "*I* didn't want — what do you mean *I* didn't want? It was you who said the neighborhood wasn't good enough. Don't you put words in my mouth, Mildred."

"Everybody knows you have no taste or background," she was replying. "Your Uncle Harry built his nest over a slaughterhouse."

And I laughed to myself. These are the wounds that never heal. This is psychological warfare as it should be fought.

Two days later, Thom came running into my study in the garage.

"The nest," he cried. "Look at the nest."

I bolted for the door. The ospreys in jealous rage were dive-bombing my whooping crane, but all they could accomplish was the breaking of their talons on the hard surface of the plaster. Finally they gave up and flew away, followed by my shouts of derision.

I did hear my oldest boy say to his brother, "Father has been working too hard. He has gone nuts."

Catbird replied, "His id has been ruptured. Sometimes one broods too much on a subject and throws the whole psychic pattern into an uproar."

That isn't quite where it rests.

It is true that the ospreys have not attacked anymore, but we have had other visitors, human visitors.

One morning I looked out the window to see a rather stout lady in khaki trousers and a turtleneck sweater creeping across my lawn on her hands and knees. Field glasses dangled from her neck and she held a camera in front of her. When I went out to question her, she angrily waved me away.

"Go back," she whispered hoarsely. "Do you want her to fly away?"

"But you don't understand — "I began.

"*Will* you keep your voice down," she said hoarsely. "Do you know what that is? The club will never believe me. If I don't get a picture of her I'll kill you."

Yes, we have had bird watchers — lots of them. You see, our whooping crane can be sighted from a long way off. After a time they discovered the nature of the thing, but they would not listen to my explanation of the ruse.

In fact, they became angry, not at the ospreys, where the blame rests — but at me.

As I write, it is autumn of 1956 and from the coldness and the growing winds, an early winter and a cold one is indicated. I have taken my whooping crane down and restored the nest to its old beauty. When the spring comes again — we shall see what we shall see. No one can say that I am unforgiving. The nest is ready and waiting. Let us see whether the ospreys are big enough to let bygones be bygones.

My wife says that if she has to go through another year like this she will — no, I won't tell you what she says. Sometimes her sense of humor seems a little strained.

The Way We Were

William Mulvihill

I'm having this problem with Sag Harbor summer nightlife, can't quite get used to the number of people on Main Street, ten o'clock, eleven, even later. People of all ages strolling, shopping, standing in groups, going in and out of stores, restaurants, the Wharf Shop, bars, ice cream places, you name it. Amazing.

A big difference from the Main Street I remember. Then the stores would close at five and the only people you'd see would be going to the movies or hanging around The Paradise. There were no restaurants. Stores dealt in basics. You shopped at the Fil-Net, Ivan's shoe store, Barry's. You went to Nick Conca or to Alioto's for a haircut. You bought groceries at Raltons or Korsaks. There weren't any places to buy souvenirs, or polo gear or art, no stores on Long Wharf because there wasn't a wharf, only an abandoned dock with missing planks.

Sag Harbor then was an isolated hamlet surrounded by woodlands. No Wickatuck, no Azurest, no Bay Point, no houses in Mount Misery, none along Brick Kiln Road. North Haven had old mansions like Maycroft and those on Actors Colony Road, some farms like Laskowski's and Kondratow-icz's, but very few year-round houses like you see over by the ferry or around Fresh Pond. Sag Harbor had no suburbs.

We'd always been a port but few boats came. This was before the Barrys created their docks and before Marine Park.

———

The movie house was new and for forty cents you saw *Gone With The Wind* and *Gunga Din*. The American Hotel was abandoned. Cormaria was empty. The interesting brick railroad station was torn down to make way for the post office. The old bridge to North Haven was replaced.

Latham House was Woodward Brothers, a general store that even then belonged to a bygone era. Lincoln would have felt at home there. I'd go to buy a five-pound bag of cracked corn for my pigeons and watch one of the elderly men take a handscoop, open a wooden barrel and fill a paper bag on an ancient scale. Twenty-five cents.

Sag Harbor Rose was a gas station. Where there's antique shops there was Harry Youngs, who fixed cars and my bicycle. Spitz's store was on the corner, the only place where you could buy phonograph records, those old 78's: Tommy Dorsey, Glen Miller, Benny Goodman.

We more or less had our own style of talk, a kind of subculture vocabulary. We'd been a port for a long time and most families still had some connection with the water so there were maritime words and references embedded in our everyday speech. Somebody who was drunk was *three sheets*

Fred Hines conducts

in the wind. Something stuck was *Jackson'd*, taking firewood that wasn't yours was *piratin'*. We used terms that you now don't hear too much: *stick an oar in, show your colors, marooned, bailout, shipshape, raise the wind, stow it, know the ropes, any port in a storm, the cut of his jib, greenhorn*. Someone sick could be described as *too weak to push a heron off the tongs*. You could be as happy *as a clam in high water*.

The village then had a lot of Irish and our ordinary speech was indebted

to the Emerald Isle. A fool was an *omadhoun*. And because most of the Irish were Catholics that too was a source of words and phrases. *God only knows* suggested doubt. Anyone who hurried from place to place was *like a dog at a fair*. Unruly boys were *hooligans* or perhaps *blaggards*. A moment of travail might call for *Jesus, Mary and Joseph*. A suffering person was *like Christ on the Cross*. A sick child might have *eyes like two burnt holes in a blanket*. Idle talk was *lally-gaging*. Someone unfocused could be a *blatherskyte*. A sad person was *heart-scalded*. An old person acting younger than his or her years might better *be home saying his prayers*. You could be as proud as *Billy-be-damned* or as queer as *Dick's hatband*. You might have more problems than you could *shake a stick at*.

Most houses needed work but the Depression was still going and there wasn't any money for repairs, additions or even paint. If something needed work you did it yourself or asked your brother-in-law to help. There was no such thing as landscapers; you cut your own lawn with a lawnmower. The lack of money could have been, in the long run, beneficial. We grew up in a village that was slowly falling apart but the lack of money might have prevented those who owned historic houses from destroying them in a frenzy of remodeling.

A large number of people — probably the majority — in the village were related by blood, close marital ties or distant relationships. Large families married into other large families. People tended to marry their classmates. You could trace kinship with ease: your grandmother was a cousin of your nephew's wife who, by the way, was, through her sister...

Nobody traveled much. Only a few people had cars and there was no L.I.E. On top of that nobody had the money. People lived in the house they'd been born in.

If you weren't related to somebody, you knew something about him or her. You didn't see many people in town that you hadn't seen before. One of my relatives, on seeing three people on Main Street he didn't recognize might observe that there were a lot of strangers in town...

This would change with World War II. Veterans brought back girls from Boston, England, Germany, even Australia.

We didn't know much about our long and rich history, didn't know that Sag Harbor had been an Indian village or occupied by British troops during the Revolution, that a battle was fought here. Nor did we know that scores of local boys had fought in the same company in the Civil War.

Sag Harbor is still pretty much the way it was and much improved. Long Wharf is a delight. We have Canio's. We have the Long Pond Greenbelt. We have Nancy Boyd Willey Park as a green gateway. The *Sag Harbor Express* goes on and on. We have an historic district. We have CONPOSH and the South Fork Groundwater Task Force and the Legion. We have a Tree Committee. We have an Historical Society. Bay Street is fun. The Library is better. We're working on the Whaling Museum, the Old Burying Ground. Let's be thankful for what we've got — and protect it.

Movie Project in Development at the American Hotel at 2 A.M.

Mark Ciabattari

A beautiful woman alone at that table in the corner, Rizzoli thinks, as he glances around the back dining room at the American Hotel. *Another single woman at that other table, too. Intellectual-looking woman.*

Harold and I and the two women are the only persons still having dinner this late tonight. Fans in this back room, hot night. What time is it anyway? No clock.

Rizzoli has grown tired here during dinner from listening to Harold present *yet another of these endless Hamptons development deals. Everything is development projects here in the Hamptons in summer, each one needing investors to complete. Nothing finished.*

Empty tables wait with white tablecloths, starched napkins and wicker chairs as Rizzoli glances around the vacant end of the room, then at the wall with its nineteenth-century prints against patterned rose wallpaper.

"Rizzoli," Harold, the well-known Oscar-winning movie producer, says, against the soft strains of Gershwin coming from the baby grand in the other dining room, "so, let me give you more details about this development deal of mine." Harold stops speaking; his mouth is full.

Rizzoli waits politely and, while using his fish knife deftly on his grilled swordfish, he studies the famous producer. He sees a stylish older man with classical features setting off his short-cropped Roman-like hair. Harold is in casually elegant summer attire: a coral-colored linen jacket, white pants and pastel tie.

"Rizzoli," Harold says in his deep voice, "in the movie business, to continue being successful, I've had to keep setting trends, taking the giant leap ahead. This project is in that vein exactly — so exciting, it is going to reshape movie viewing for years to come. What's more…"

Rizzoli isn't listening; he's glanced down to see what he himself is wearing. He's surprised, *It's my style at least.* A Matisse tie with a light olive double-breasted sport coat. Light blue shirt.

Confident about his dress and eating well with his fish knife, Rizzoli is relieved to think, *Maybe I've become more of a gentleman and less nouveau riche than I was a few weeks ago, when I became an instant multimillionaire and came out to the Hamptons.*

"…So, I want you to have the chance to get in on the deal early," Harold is saying, "after all you might wind up being my son-in-law so, it'd be in the family."

Rizzoli is still not paying attention. Instead, he is looking across to the far garden-court dining room at a big mirror with his and Harold's reflections. *And the intellectual woman's.*

Over his own head's reflection, Rizzoli sees the green digital numbers flashing his worth, instant to instant, in mirror image. Rizzoli reads it backward. *$720 million and something is my total worth — a drop from a week ago but rising again.*

"So, tell me more," Rizzoli says, trying to be polite.

As Harold continues talking about his movie deal, what Rizzoli really notices is Harold's stroking you-are-so-key-to-this-project tone of voice. Rizzoli is amused that *ever since I've had these fake millions over my head, people like Harold play to me… see me as key, these important Hamptons types.*

Rizzoli never used to be treated like this by these people. *Now, I've come to expect it. It's changing me.*

The Hulbert house (1796), Union Street. "Summer White House" of Chester Arthur, 1881–1884.

Truth is... Rizzoli can't fool himself. He's still worth only $1,714. He knows that for a fact. *I've known that all along.*

Why fool Harold? Why not try telling him the truth? Rizzoli can't. He knows why. *I'm still in the grip of appearances.*

What's more... Rizzoli has a vague memory (*from somewhere*) of when he tried to tell people the truth, they just laughed and chose, instead, to believe what their eyes told them.

"Harold, so you were saying about your project in development," Rizzoli repeats. "Sorry, my mind wandered for an instant there."

Harold looks miffed for a split second but smiles and says, "Yes, as I was explaining, you're aware I'm sure that my last film project grossed $110 million but you don't know the real budget..."

REAL?

"...real budget for that film was only $40 million, NOT..."

It was padded.

"...NOT the $60 million that was reported in the trades. So, you figure it — more insider's profit.

"This movie is supposed, SUPPOSED... to cost $80 million, REAL BUDGET? Forty-five. Fifty mil.

"YET, it will also earn more. Why, Rizzoli? It's true to life. So true, the moviemaking will be reinvented... in the process..."

Moviemaking... REINVENTED?

"...so, as an independent producer, I need a guy with deep pockets, willing to dare, a guy precisely like you, Rizzoli. What do you say?"

"What I'm willing to do is this," Rizzoli answers, startling himself by beginning to propose something he doesn't know what, "when I decide to leave our dinner this evening, I'll invest my gain, provided my worth has registered a gain for this evening."

Harold smiles agreeably.

"My base worth was $718 million — that was what it registered when we walked in here to have dinner. So, what am I worth now, Harold?"

Harold glances up over Rizzoli's head. "$720 million."

"Up two million," Rizzoli adds, suddenly having the insight about why he's proposed this — he wants to get this dinner over but not seem impolite to the famous producer.

"So, Harold, what do you say we call it an evening?"

Rizzoli can see Harold looks disappointed. *Listen to him a little while longer*, Rizzoli urges himself. *That way he'll be happy, yet my worth won't go up a lot more. Two million is about what I'm comfortable investing, at any rate.*

"We'll keep talking a little while more, Harold, if you like, just remember, I can't guarantee my numbers won't disappear into thin air, and if so, you lose. But, with this two-million-dollar gain, I'll write you a check here and now." *What? Your millions are all the bank's computer error, you know that. You don't have that kind of money. You're acting the role of Big Shot,... playing the market.*

"If you don't mind, I'd like to keep talking," Harold says, grateful at the offer to speculate in Rizzoli a little more.

"So, what about the script?" Rizzoli asks boldly, hoping to direct the conversation and not have Harold ramble on endlessly about his development project. "Tell me."

Harold explains the current scriptwriter is "fantastic. Name is Theresa. She's a high-key, nervous sort. Rewrites a lot. Sees everything as a movie, Incredible.

"The script is being finished. Theresa has it all up to this point. It's more real than a movie, I tell you. Here, take a look at this," Harold says, reaching into his fine leather slipcase and pulling out a script. "Take a glance. It's the script to date."

Rizzoli puts on his glasses and glances at the front page. It reads:

WHICH IS IT? NIGHT? OR DAY?

AN ORIGINAL SCREENPLAY BY THERESA ULMAN

HIGH ANGLE SHOT OF MAGICIAN

He strides with authority, laughing, on modern-day Main Street, with the village's nineteenth-century, three-story brick building, a hotel, in the foreground.

CAMERA LOWERS. CAMERA ZOOMS IN.

BEGIN TITLES OVER busy summery Main Street with pass-ersby.

CLOSE SHOT — MAGICIAN

MAGICIAN

This moment is the highlight of all the time before and after, if you know this right moment before it's past.

What? Rizzoli flips to the last page of the script as Harold says, "The dialogue there is fresh, honest," Rizzoli reads the last lines of dialogue:

> THE PRODUCER
> The dialogue there is fresh, honest.

> THE INVESTOR
> Yes.

Rizzoli looks up and says, "Yes," then reads:

> THE PRODUCER
> What's in the script there really plays, as we say in the business.

Rizzoli looks up, as Harold looks his way and says, "What's in the script there really plays — Harold moves his fingers to make quotes around the word — "as we say in the business."

"Uh-huh," Rizzoli says, reading "THE INVESTOR: Uh-huh."

"In fact," Harold says, "the scriptwriter Theresa, happens to be the woman sitting over there at the other table now."

Rizzoli glances up in the mirror and sees Harold's indicated she's the intellectual-looking woman. Rizzoli focuses on the reflection of this scriptwriter, who is unaware she is being observed. So Rizzoli studies her intense expression. He can almost sense her mind working.

"Right now she's working out what's next, seeing a scene, hearing dialogue. You can bet on it," says Harold. "If she wasn't working, I'd introduce you."

What Harold said just then… is not dialogue in her mind, is it? Harold and I are not in her mind, voices making up dialogue for this scene she wants. We're not spectres she fantasizes in a scene not yet written, are we?, Rizzoli wonders….

He calms himself by telling himself he's really experiencing nothing unusual and, in fact, he's just back finishing dinner with Harold and *the close-up mirror is imaginary, the figures pure fantasy. Nothing real.*

Rizzoli closes his eyes and takes comfort in recalling the solid feeling he had just moments ago, *When I was at a steady $720 million.* He wishes his worth were down there again, instead of going up so high he can't relate. He wishes it'd be back at 720.

Rizzoli still has his eyes closed but feels his giant fish lips wanting to say, "Harold. I've got to go now. So, what's the gain?"

He opens his eyes. The mirror says $1.8 billion. Huge-faced Harold is talking on.

Harold's scriptwriter, has Harold… taking millions in… in talk. She's not giving me the line, "I've got to go, Harold."

What's behind all this? Rizzoli wonders and a deep voice (*OFF-SCREEN? A NARRATOR?*) answers, "Behind all this… is NOTHING. The VOID."

The White Rabbit

Joe Hanna

It was snowing outside. The door rattled open and Bill Porter entered. He had things in his hand. Some of the things were tools and some of the things were wires and dangly bits. He had arrived to add something to the security system, something that would sense when pipes were about to freeze. It would (and did) raise the alarm.

"Hey, Bill!"

I enjoy visits with Bill. He remembers interesting times from olden days, the days of the Black Buoy.

The other day he was telling the tale of two locals who decided to streak the American Hotel. It is a famous local story. The incident was hatched, if that is the right term, at the bar behind the black door with the weird porthole. The village had reached a crossroads and nothing better illustrated the shape and directions of the crossroads than the cold winter's night that two men ran naked from the Black Buoy across the street to the hotel and they kept going right into the subdued lighting and fireplace flicker and candle glow within.

People talked revolution in those days. Rebellion! Down with convention! The streakers pictured in their addled minds tables full of uptight WASP Victorians who would faint when confronted by nakedity. The irony is that the diners were reading *Couples* and had probably produced *Hair* or acted in or reviewed it. And at least one of the people at the bar had invented

the term Gonzo journalism. The streakers were the reactionaries. The diners were the architects of the sexual revolution. But that particular irony went the way of all flash. The streakers had fortified themselves to the point of insensibility at the bar before their mission. Jose Cuervo and Jim Beam are lousy reporters. They are better spin doctors.

"Oh, man! You schooood have...sheen them. Women screamed! Jaws were dropped I'm telling you! I guess we showed 'em...dinnnnt we?"

One of the streakers attempting to exercise a dubious exit strategy ran into a small, but unforgiving part of the historic building. Bonk! He replicated the spread eagle motif; the logo parentis of the Hotel. It was a slapstick end to a show of farce.

The subtext of the streak was that Dodge City was slowly being gentrified. The shock jog was the plaintive swan thong of colorful and troubled locals beating their tiny fists against the huge treasure chest of Daddy Warbucks who was moving in for the real estate killing to come. "Oh spirit, tell me that these things need not come to pass and that with application and a case of cold Bud we might yet hold back these dreadful portents, these future dreams of dried-leaf brittle men who blow across our dark streets like crab shadows."

"Sorry. I calls it like I sees it. My advice to you is to get a German car. Oh and by the way…"

"Yes?"

"Tiny Tim and Miss Vicki will never make it as a couple."

"Oh, spirit! Say not so! What can be done?"

"Done? Haven't you done enough already?"

I suppose I had done quite enough already. I worked on the crew that reconditioned the old American Hotel. By knocking down walls to make groups of three rooms into single rooms and by adding modern baths, not down the hall but right there in the room, I had played my little part in making the hotel a fit place for persons of taste and discretion (and of stout plastic) to unwind from the various tumults encountered in the upper levels of brokerage and management.

The age of the Hotel was dawning. The age of the Black Buoy was drawing to a close; dusk to dusk and asses to asses.

Still, our naked reactionaries had carried the flag into the very innermost keep of the enemy's fortress.

Yes. The old days. The days when getting naked had at least the possibility of inspiring procreative scheming and air-shaking erotic tension. You could feel it in the back room of the Black Buoy. Longings flitted out from the dark recesses like bats released by sundown. The longings beat the air above impassive faces and made the light seem to flicker. Maybe, just maybe…tonight…someone…maybe that one at the end of the bar…hmmmmmm…not a bad profile…

Naked in public. A crowd-pleaser suitable for any blue light occasion.

"You should have seen 'em! I guess we showed 'em. Man!"

As good as the moment was, there was a technical problem with streaking. It happens too quickly. There is no time for a mood to develop. This problem was mulled over by members of a small elite group who met at the Buoy and called themselves The Garden Party. It was a woman known to me only as The White Rabbit who solved this knotty problem by creating The Snail. If a streak was designed to startle, The Snail was invented to generate. The trick was to see how slow you could go and still have a show. It helped to stand on the bar.

"I think her name was Leslie. I'll have to ask Sonja or Judy Long," said Bill. His eyes were misted over with recollective fog. "I think she lived at the Morpurgo House."

The Morpurgo house! I shuddered. I was once, a long time ago, asked to do some carpentry work in there. When I went to inspect the premises and

to begin to sketch out a budget, I realized that the scope of the work needed was beyond my abilities, beyond the abilities of most earthly powers. Perhaps on that very day, somewhere over my head, above the cracked and peeling plaster and sagging floor joists, the White Rabbit lay curled in her comforter dreaming what dreams that Rabbits may and Leslies dare not speak of.

"The snail," I said.

"Oh, yes," said Bill.

Sag Harbor in its latest calm period before being rediscovered was uniquely congenial. There were no functioning locks on our house on Howard Street and none were needed even the night a drunk staggered into the downstairs bedroom and passed out. He thought he was at his girlfriend's house. He was only off by a few doors and one street. Not bad shooting for a guy who was so drunk he needed to hold onto the grass to lean against the ground.

No harm was done. Life is messy. It is fantasy that must be walled off to protect it. Theme parks have fences and pay gates.

71

Our village used to be populated by a nice mix of musicians for whom my brother coined the term "guitarpenters", writers, factory hands, baymen, shopkeepers, short-order cooks, antiques sellers, gentility on the way down and land-owning locals on the way up. You could find a comfortable social niche and enjoy it without putting down those who found other accommodations. It was remarkably free of stratification. I never had anyone lecture me in those days about how things ought to be or how sorry we all were. People understood that life is tough and you do what you can and some fail and some fail spectacularly. Love was often expressed as humor. They are as closely related as fear and hate are intertwined. I don't think you can have love without a sense of humor. The anti-matter of humor (and love) is self-importance.

The days of harmless nakedity are gone, alas. There is a new ethos in town. It could be crudely expressed as, "You want to see these buster? You are going to have to pay; big time."

And so it goes.

The Soul of Summer

Paul Ruffins

At least once every year, twice if I'm lucky, I violate a minor local ordinance, and walk down the wooded hill behind my family's summer house in Ninevah Beach, in Sag Harbor.

The ground, which drops away fairly steeply, is perpetually carpeted in half a foot of dead leaves. After 35 summers, I know my way through these woods by instinct and I can tread quietly and smoothly down the incline. The forest that grows from the sandy soil is about equal parts scrub oak and sassafras, so the woods are low but densely green under the strong sun illuminating the ceiling of leaves. As I move among the trees, the tips of their branches reach toward me. And although they do not touch me, their effect is palpable; just to pass through this familiar patch of woodland is soothing, and I feel the tension lift.

A few hundred yards farther I pass the thin line of pines marking where the ground becomes too wet for trees at Little Northwest Creek that runs in from Shelter Island Sound. As the hill flattens out, the quality of the light brightens, and the horizon shifts from the verticals of the woods to the wider, horizontal sightlines of the marsh and the sound, half a mile beyond. The cushioned earth becomes swampy sand, and the ground cover changes from leaves to salt grass. The creek, which rises and falls with the tides, feeds the saltwater marsh and forms the natural boundary to the east end of Ninevah Beach.

Lincoln Street, the Ninevah Beach development's longest, is the last road within the town limits of Sag Harbor, a former whaling port, and home of one of the most vibrant black resort communities in the United States.

Somewhere behind me, far up the hill, is a little green sign saying that the area is restricted. If I am an outlaw, at least I am polite. I never smoke in the woods, and, as they say in the Boy Scouts, I take nothing but photographs and leave nothing but footprints. But I grew up in these parts long before the little green signs did, and sometimes I need to come home....

The African–American enclave is made up of six developments that are home to several hundred families with a summer population that swells to 1,000. Growing out from the east edge of town and stretching inland from the beach to Route 114 are Azurest, the oldest section, followed by Sag Harbor Hills and finally Ninevah. South of the highway are Lighthouse Lane, Chatfield Hills and Hillside Terrace.

Because most of the developments are about 50 years old, their social history can be contained within a human memory. Just as in other new small towns it is still possible to remember the first owner of every house on a street. As I walk out of the woods along the edge of the creek toward the beach, I encounter the first, and then, about 150 yards away, the former home, of the late Jim and Barbara Brannen. It was the Brannens who convinced my parents to buy a lot in 1957 and showed them how a black city worker could afford a summer home in one of the nicest places in the world.

The Brannens are the spiritual godparents of Ninevah Beach. Looking east toward Ninevah from the long wharf in town, the Brannens' house is the last building you can see on the beach. From the bay, looking inland along the creek, you can see their original pink and white house. The house closest to the wetlands, it's where my family spent weekends years before building our own house....

Jim Brannen was a New York City fireman and part-time contractor. When Azurest and Sag Harbor Hills began to take off, he became the real estate agent for Ninevah Beach and sold lots through his circle of friends and acquaintances who included a lot of firefighters, like my dad.

"When we first started in the early 1950s, beachfront properties were $3,000," says Barbara Brannen. "The other lots were $750 which meant you could buy for $250 down and $35 a month."

Brannen built most of his first house himself. Scores of his friends, like my parents, would bring their families here for barbecues and long weekends, the logical prelude to buying a lot and getting their own place.

My parents bought their lot even though they questioned their ability to build a house on a fireman's salary with my mother staying home to look after six children. In 1965, they sold a share to my Uncle Reynold and his wife Joan, and hired a contractor to erect a shell — four walls, a roof, plumbing and electricity. I remember being able to see through every room on the first floor. It looked like a forest of two-by-fours surrounding a bathtub. My father and uncle did the finishing work themselves.

Several other families also bought shells they finished themselves, and a few struggling artists and architects built homes of their own design, or from plans ordered from *Popular Mechanics* magazine. Sometimes people camped in their houses while they built up around themselves.

But we were the exception. Many of the earliest investors were doctors, entrepreneurs and others who made up New York's black elite before World War II. They could afford second homes almost as easily as their white counterparts.

Most of my friends' parents were college-educated people with city government jobs; sometimes it seemed to me that all their mothers were teachers. As a group, they greatly benefited from the high wages and low inflation of the late '50s and '60s. Most believed it was better to sacrifice for a summer house than to buy yourself a new car every few years. Only the doctors could do both.

Today, most of the black folks who own property here consider Sag Harbor their handmade slice of the American pie. Their beach is the heart and the

Pink house, Ninevah

crossroads of this community. Topographically, its a family affair. The shore is shallow for more than 100 feet out. Along a gently curving stretch of Shelter Island Sound, the waves never rise above a slight chop, and there is no undertow. As teenagers in search of more exciting swimming, my friends and I would ride our bicycles six miles over to the beach at Sagaponack, on the ocean side of the South Fork, closer to East Hampton. At night we came back to our beach to shoot off firecrackers or make out in the darkness. Like walking in the preserve, firecrackers are now frowned upon. Romance, however, remains largely unregulated.

As I walk west along the beach, I encounter a friend I've known since childhood — Steven Roach, a financial manager for a nonprofit association who also has been summering here since his parents built their house in the mid-'60s. "We're lucky to have something like this," he says, sweeping his hand to indicate the whole shoreline. The beachfront properties range from lovely '50s ranch houses to much newer, bigger homes with trendy architectural details such as cedar shingles, oversized skylights and sprawling decks that almost reach to the high water line. Clean sand defines the water's edge, where families, small sailboats and the occasional Jet Ski are in evidence.

Roach's allusion to "we" refers to more than him and me. He means a larger community whose affection for the place comes from common intangible experience. Like me, he is as comfortable sending his child down to this beach alone as my parents were in sending me. In this community, older people who don't know my first name still recognize me as one of those Ruffins children. In this community, if you leave a bicycle or a pair of sunglasses on the sand, it will be there tomorrow.

Sag Harbor's contemporary black developments evolved out of Eastville, the 18th-century community of free blacks and Native Americans who grew up along with the whaling industry that was Sag Harbor's commercial centerpiece from the American Revolution to the end of the Civil War.

Despite the danger, harsh conditions and low wages, sailing attracted black freemen to the adventure of life at sea. In *Moby Dick*, Herman Melville accurately depicted an interracial New England whaling crew, and early local records indicate that 20% to 30% of Sag Harbor's sailors were either black or

Native American. Together, they built the "colored" community of Eastville, where Native Americans played an important role in founding St. David's AME Zion Church in 1840, the town's first "colored" congregation.

By the early 1900s, Eastville was attracting visitors from New York City, mainly middle-class black folks escaping the summer heat of Brooklyn. One such visitor — Maud Kenny Meredith Terry — forged the direct link between Eastville and the contemporary black community it spawned to the north and east.

Born in 1887, Terry spent summers in Sag Harbor in the 1930s. She sought out the owner of the tract of land between Eastville and the beach on Shelter Island Sound, who agreed to subdivide the property and permit Terry to sell lots through her personal contacts, mostly doctors, ministers and business-people. The first land survey was completed in 1947, and Terry named it Azurest. Then she named the streets after members of her family and notable figures in African–American history such an President Lincoln and black ship builder Paul Cuffee.

During the '50s and '60s the construction of the black summer places helped the still-unfashionable town remain solvent when it lost industrial jobs with the closing of the Bulova Watch factory and the Grumman aircraft plant. Decades later, in the 1990s, Sag Harbor has become hipper, fortu-itously sprouting a sushi bar at about the same time I developed a taste for raw fish.

Today the younger black professionals buying homes or inheriting their par-ents' properties often have corporate jobs and much more money than time. However, many in the previous generation have decided to live there full time instead of only during the summer. After 27 years of sharing a house with my parents, my Uncle Reynold, an art professor and children's book illustrator, bought his own house halfway between Ninevah Beach and Eastville on Route 114. With the help of a fax machine and express mail he lives in Sag Harbor year-round, commuting to New York City only on the days he teaches.

St. David's A.M.E. Zion Church

Some longtime residents confronted with new problems — too many Jaguars, too few parking spaces — believe the town suffers from being too trendy. But far more of us share Barbara Brannen's feeling that the town's current popularity validates the black pioneers' original vision. "When we first came out here in the late 1940s, black folks wanted a place of their own because you knew you weren't welcome everywhere. Today, if you've got the money, it's totally different. We're proud that black folks who can afford to vacation anywhere, still choose to come here."

from The Man in My Basement

Walter Mosley

"Mr. Blakey?" the small white man asked.

I had answered the door expecting big Clarance Mayhew and his cousin Ricky. The three of us had a standing date to play cards on Thursday nights. I was surprised even to hear the doorbell because it was too early for my friends to have made it home from work and neither one of them would have rung the bell anyway. We'd been friends since childhood, since my grandparents owned the house.

"My house is your house," I always said to Clarance and Ricky. I never locked the door because we lived in a secluded colored neighborhood way back from the highway. Everybody knows everybody in my neighborhood, so strangers don't go unnoticed. If somebody stole something from me, I'd have known who it was, what kind of car he drove, and the numbers on his license plate before he was halfway to Southampton.

"Yes," I said to the small, bald-headed white man in the dark-green suit. "I'm Blakey."

"You have a stand-up basement, Mr. Blakey," the white man told me.

"Say what?"

"Teddy Odett down at Odett Realty said that you had a basement where a man could stand fully erect, one that has electricity and running water."

"This house isn't for sale, mister."

"Bennet, Anniston Bennet. I'm from Greenwich, Connecticut."

"Well this house isn't for sale, Mr. Bennet." I thought the small man would hunch his shoulders, or maybe give me a mean frown if he was used to getting his way. Either way I expected him to leave.

"Oh yes," he said instead. "I know that. Your family has owned this beautiful home for seven generations or more. Mr. Odett told me that. I know it isn't for sale. I'm interested in renting."

"Renting? Like an apartment?"

The man made a face that might have been a smile, or an apology. He let his head loll over his right shoulder and blinked while showing his teeth for a moment.

"Well, not exactly," he said. "I mean yes but not in the conventional way."

His body moved restlessly but his feet stayed planted as if he were a child who was just learning how to speak to adults.

"Well it's not for rent. It's just an old basement. More spiders down there than dust and there's plenty'a dust."

Mr. Bennet's discomfort increased with my refusal. His small hands clenched as if he were holding onto a railing against high winds.

I didn't care. That white man was a fool. We didn't take in white boarders in my part of the Sag Harbor. I was trying to understand why the real-estate agent Teddy Odett would even refer a white man to my neighborhood.

"I want to rent your basement for a couple of months this summer, Mr. Blakey."

"I just told you —"

"I can make it very much worth your while."

It was his tone that cut me off. Suddenly he was one of those no-nonsense-white-men-in-charge. What he seemed to be saying was "I know something that you had better listen to, fool. Here you think you know what's going on when really you don't have a clue."

I knew that there were white people in the Hamptons that rented their homes for four and five thousand dollars a month over the summer. I owned a home like that. It was three stories high and about two hundred years old.

It was in excellent shape too. My father had worked at keeping it *up to code*, as he'd say, for most of his life.

"I'm sorry, Mr. Bennet," I said again.

"I'm willing to pay quite a bit for what I want, Mr. Blakey," the white man said.…

After my coffee I drove down to the old *highway*, a graded dirt road that led to Canyon's Field. It was the shortcut that would take me most of the way to Wilson Ryder's construction site. The Ryder family had lived in the Harbor for more than 150 years, a long time but not nearly as long as my folks had been around. But you couldn't tell them that. Wilson liked to tell people that his family helped to settle the east end of the island.

Both sides of my family had lived in that area as early as 1742. The Blakeys were indentured servants who earned their freedom. The Dodds were free from the beginning. It was even hinted that they, the Dodds, came straight from Africa at the beginning of the eighteenth century. My parents were both very proud that their ancestors were never slaves. The only time I had ever seen my father get angry was when Clarance's father once asked him, "How can you be sure that one'a them Blakeys you so proud of wasn't a slave at one time or other?"

It was a lovely ride. The woods were deep and green down that way. There were three or four ponds in walking distance from the side of the road. I decided that I'd go fishing after asking Wilson for a job. I planned to tell him that I could begin working that next Monday. That way I could have a long weekend before going back to a job.

A group of eight or nine deer was crossing the road a ways up from me. I came to a stop and so did they. The big female looked at me with hard eyes, trying to glean my intentions. A sigh escaped my throat. I loved to watch deer watching me. They were so timid and ignorant of everything but the possible threat. People think that they're cowardly, but I've been charged by a male or two. I respected them, because with no defense except for their quick feet, they lived out in the wild with no law or protection.

I once saw a group of fifteen or more of them swimming out to Shelter Island. Their heads just above the water, they looked frightened and desperate out there. Cowards don't face terror. Cowards live on back roads, behind closed doors, with the TVs blasting out anything to keep the silence and the darkness from intruding.

The deer's caution made them move slower than they would have without my presence. I enjoyed the show. When the final white tail bobbed off into the wood, I was thoroughly satisfied.

My uncle Brent had been a hunter before he got sick. He killed hundreds of deer down in South Carolina, where he'd lived with his third wife.

"Hunt for the weekend hunters," he'd tell me in one of his few friendly moods. "Kill six bucks and make two forty."

When I was a child I imagined that the deer used to surround our house in the evening, hoping that Brent would come outside for a walk. Then they could stomp him to death for the crimes he'd committed against their race.

"Chuck," Wilson Ryder said. The tone of his voice mimicked surprise, but it was also leveled at me offensively.

"Mr. Ryder," I said in greeting. I hated the name Chuck. And he knew it because I had asked him not to call me by that name eighteen years before when I had my first summer job working for his family's construction company.

Wilson Ryder was an older white man with yellowish white hair and a big gut. His family had been in construction for three generations. Young men in my family had worked for his family almost the whole time. He had gray eyes, and fingers covered with yellow-and-black calluses from hard work and cigarettes.

We were standing in a wide circle of yellow soil that had been cleared out of a scrub-pine stand. The trees stood in an angry arc three hundred yards from the center of the circle. There were the beginnings of excavation here and there. Enough to give you the idea of the cul-de-sac of mansions that the Ryder family intended to build. They would level the whole island and sell it off stone by stone if they could.

"What can I do for you?" Ryder asked me.

"I'd like a job, Mr. Ryder."

His gray eyes squinted a hundredth of an inch, maybe less, but it was enough to say that he wasn't going to hire me. Even more than that, the pained wince said that he wouldn't hire me, not because there was no job but because there was something wrong somewhere — something wrong with me....

"No jobs," he said with a one-shoulder shrug.

I could tell that Ryder wanted me to disappear, just as I had felt about the white man at my door the day before. But I wasn't going to go away that easily. My family had given Wilson's grandfather one of his first jobs. My grandmother delivered Wilson's brother and sister. He couldn't whisper two words and expect me to go away just like that.

"Well?" he said.

"I thought you had just started hiring."

"It's hard times, Charlie," he said. "You got to get there first if you want to work nowadays."

"But somebody told me last night that you'd still be hiring today."

"Well," Ryder began.

He was ready to carry his lie further. But then he looked at me, really I think he was looking at himself, wondering why the hell he was going through all those changes over some unemployed local Negro.

"You used to work for that bank, didn't ya?" he asked.

"Yeah?"

"Why aren't you there anymore?"

"I don't know. They just let me go."

"Well let's just say that I'm lettin' you go too."

It didn't make any sense. How could he let me go if I didn't even work for him? I almost said something about it, but I knew that I'd just sound stupid.

Wilson gave me a crooked little smile and friendly nod. *Can't win 'em all* — that's what the gesture meant.

I cursed him all the way down the road to the town of Sag Harbor.

from Life So Far: A Memoir

Betty Friedan

In the midst of the battle for the ERA, I bought a house in the old whaling village of Sag Harbor. I had been renting one house after another since the commune broke up — a house in East Hampton which was so unsummery that my friend Susan Wood, a photographer, brought over armsful of colorful sheets she was shooting for a manufacturer's brochure and we covered all the chairs and couches with them and hung them as curtains. That house was known as the House of Sheets. Then I rented another house with a friend, but that didn't work out very well because she had a nervous breakdown. The last house I rented before I started looking for a home of my own was a little guest house in Wainscott next door to my friends the Roses.

I found the house I live in now on the first day I looked. I saw three houses that day (one, a huge corner house down the street that my friends Richard and Kathy Reeves bought a few weeks later) and chose a modest saltbox that had been built by a ship's carpenter in the *Moby-Dick* era. It was bigger than it seemed from the street and sat on one-third of an acre ending in Sag Harbor Cove. Over the years, I would enlarge the kitchen, turn what had been a side stoop into a long dining area and merge a shed to make a writing and sitting area. I also broke through into the attic to make a sleeping loft and created another loft over the kitchen.

Buying the house was one of the smartest things I've ever done. I started going out to Sag Harbor every weekend unless I had something big to do in

Glover Street

New York. It became home for me and a favorite hangout for my kids, especially when they started having kids of their own. I can sleep fourteen in the
house, with the seven grandkids in the lofts.

Shortly after I bought the house, I got a call from *Newsday*, the Long Island
newspaper. "We're doing a feature on Sag Harbor," the reporter said. "How did
you know Sag Harbor was going to be 'in'?" "In?" The thought hadn't crossed
my mind and frankly, I didn't care. But I was always good at choosing houses
and places to live. Sag Harbor had — and still has — a strong sense of community, which I've always thought is very important. Some of my first magazine
articles were about houses and community and communal living, as was a por-
tion of *The Second Stage* which I wrote in that house in Sag Harbor.

I also agreed early on to speak at a fund-raising lunch in Sag Harbor in
support of the Jermain Library. It was not something I particularly wanted to
do — I would rather have accepted a brunch invitation for that Sunday
morning in August — but I was new to the community and wanted to
become a part of it and I believe in libraries anyway. I hadn't expected to be
attacked, however. After the lecture there was a question-and-answer period,

and this dame, who was publishing a now defunct newspaper in Sag Harbor and was quite reactionary, waved something in the air and said: "You signed the Humanist Manifesto. How dare you come into this community and preach your ideas of godlessness. Answer yes or no: do you believe in God?" It was absolutely outrageous. Of course I had signed the Humanist Manifesto which Bertrand Russell and his group had issued some years before, calling for peace, social progress and everything any reasonable person would be for. In fact, I had insisted on signing it. They had all these great men signing it and no women, so I'd called them up and said: "How come you don't have any women signing this thing?" No one would dare do that now, of course, but they were totally flustered and said: "Oh dear, oh dear. Well, would you sign it?" and I said yes.

But here was this woman waving it around, saying, "We have a woman here, influencing our children, who doesn't believe in God." I was completely taken aback. But instead of standing on my constitutional right to freedom of religion and my privacy of conscience, I found myself answering: "How dare you question my religion and my belief in God! I am proudly a

Jew, and according to my religion, I have lived my whole life in religious terms. In my religion, the Jewish religion, it is your duty to use your life to make life better for those who come after us, and I have done that by helping make life better for future generations of women and men as well."

It was an indignant but good response, I think, but this horrible woman didn't let up; not only did she continue to rant and rave about my "godlessness" in her newspaper but to write letters about my dangerous influence on the community to the other, more substantial, local weeklies. I began to get concerned after garbage was thrown on my lawn and downright nervous when I was attacked by a dog. I used to jog around Otter Pond, and one day a woman's dog started chasing me, growling and snapping at my legs. I saw the dog's owner standing on the porch and called out: "Get your dog back. Get your dog on a leash." And she said: "Why don't you go back where you came from?"

That rotten newspaper publisher was inflaming the community against me and I finally called the head of the library. "Look I was trying to be helpful to you and raise money for the library, and I don't deserve to be treated like this," I told her. "You've got to make her stop." I guess they put some pressure on her and she did finally shut up

Thank You, Ms. Betty Friedan:
You Changed America, You Changed My Life

Lorraine Dusky

We all knew she was ailing, and that her house on Glover Street in Sag Harbor was unlikely to ever again be the scene of the glamorous parties she gave in the Seventies and Eighties, corralling all the celebrated she could in her back yard.

But when the news came across AOL that Betty Friedan had died on her 85th birthday, it was a blow to the heart: the great Jeanne d'Arc of my generation was gone. She had changed America and I went along for the ride.

By the time I read *The Feminine Mystique*, in my senior year of college, I was well on my way. The heated arguments with my Midwestern, middle class parents over my career choice had given way to their grudging acceptance. They were not raising a teacher or a nurse, after all; I was a journalism major and managing editor of Wayne State University's Daily Collegian, hell-bent on a career to rival Brenda Starr's, with or without the Mystery Man.

The book pumped high-octane gas into my resolve: this woman was talking directly to me, though I didn't need to throw off the shackles of wifery. I needn't take them on at all. And I wasn't crazy and I wasn't alone.

Getting a good first job however, was something else again. I landed in a fusty women's department on a small Michigan daily where I wrote up bridals and garden features. Not exactly riveting, not exactly what I had in mind. This was the summer of 1964, one year after Friedan's ground-breaking book was published to reviews that ranged from infuriated to befuddled to laudatory.

But in the end, the reviews didn't matter: Ms. Friedan had wakened a sleeping generation of women, and millions of them would educate themselves and enter the work force with all the energy of an eruption from Etna.

Not that it was easy: men were resentful, bosses were dubious. We had to prove ourselves time and time again. When I landed a dream job the following year — general assignment reporter — I was the first woman to do so on the Rochester, New York *Democrat & Chronicle.*

I wasn't particularly brilliant; I was just aggressive enough and the right woman at the right time. I snuck in when Betty pushed the door open. Not so much that all my editors gave me decent assignments; more than the men, I had to make my own way by dreaming up assignments for myself, or spend the day on idle.

Five years later, now living in Manhattan, I was a foot-soldier among thousands of others on Fifth Avenue the day of the Women's Strike for Equality in 1970, and after the march I listened with goose-bumps and glistening eyes in Bryant Park to the words of the Mss. Friedan, Steinem, Millet and Abzug ring out with passionate oratory. We would overcome.

I would finally meet my heroine when I came to Sag Harbor. A reporter friend on *The New York Times* who had been invited to one of Betty's summer soirees took me along. With all the august types present, I was shy and hung around at the edges of the party. I was a nobody in a nice dress.

But slowly, I came to know this great personage myself — which is how I always thought of her — and when I wrote *The Best Companies for Women in 1984,* which is as it sounds, I had the nerve to ask her for a quote to put in the press release. Which she graciously gave me.

The publication party was attended by many of the women I had interviewed. Betty, of course, was the star in the room. She came to me and said, they want me to sign your book, what should I do? Sign it, of course, I said. Give them your autograph. I hope I remembered to add: You're the reason this book was even possible.

———

But for all she did for women in general, she could be amazingly rude to them in person. It was the contradiction of her life. I was the butt of her dastardly temperament myself when I was asked to help plan what came to be called the Sag Harbor Initiative, a weekend-long program of panels featuring assorted worthies from the arts, journalism, and politics, all punctuated with parties, of course, this being the Hamptons. Naturally, someone had to do the scut work, and actually bring off the weekend. Betty decided it was me. The job paid hourly wages.

She screamed instructions at me over the phone as if I were an idiot. I would tape-record them and try to make sense later of what I was supposed to do. After a couple of months — maybe only weeks but it seemed much longer — of her high-decibel shouting, I quit and was replaced by another, and then another, and another, and another. When the Initiative finally came off, one of my fellow peons, Joan Carlson — who lasted longer than the rest of us — hosted us all for lunch. I believe we were five. Of course we blathered about how terrible it was to work for Betty, and shrugged over why she, of all people, would treat women so badly. But you had to accept Betty on her own terms.

D. K. "Birdy" Holabird

The reaction in the community to the conference varied from indifference to absurd. "Scathing Liberal Politics Run Rampant at Three Day Forum Initiative" read the October 13, 1988 headline in the *Sag Harbor Express*.

But if natives were less than impressed, the Initiative, at Betty's insistence, did bring together the white and black intellectual communities of year-round "summer-people" in Sag Harbor for the duration. And the outside world paid attention: many of the conferences ran on C-SPAN. The Initiative didn't quite become the Hamptons Chautauqua that Betty envisioned, but no one doubted that it would not have happened at all without her.

One friend went to interview Betty for a publication less august than *The New York Times*, and came back furious — the great Friedan was unconscionably late, imperious, even boorish. Waiters in restaurants groaned when she walked in; store clerks tried to maintain their cool. Betty never mastered the art of being nice to the help.

Then there was the way this great feminist catered to men. It did not escape my notice that she lit up when my husband appeared. Never a beauty, now in her Sixties, she used her star power to flirt with and cater to men. Unless you were a really famous woman yourself, she was more likely to remember your husband's name than yours. But then, she never said to throw out the husband with the housework.

Despite these annoying idiosyncrasies, she could be aces as a guest, and I admit I was always pleased whenever she came to dinner. She displayed uncommon wisdom and common sense about life, world happenings, people. She loved to talk about her children — telling us how one son was a noted theoretical physicist involved with string theory, a daughter was a doctor.

For many years in Sag Harbor, you would see her jogging — shuffling, actually — around town in her purple jogging suit. She attended most events with a male companion, picked from among the famous and semi-famous writers and scientists of her acquaintance. No escort ever lasted more than a few months.

Betty might have been exasperating to some, rude to others, but she was

still: Betty Friedan, the mother of the movement, the woman who wrote that book, the sparkplug of feminism's second wave. No personal foible could diminish her achievement. She was unquestionably one of the most important figures of the 20th century. In the Women's Hall of Fame, she ranks right up there with Susan B. Anthony and Elizabeth Cady Stanton.

Dear Betty, thank you for everything. We did overcome. You changed America, and in doing so, you made the life I wanted possible. Not all the work is done yet, in many ways we're still fighting for true equality, but we're a hell of a lot farther along the road than we were before you rang the bell that woke us up.

from The Underground Stream

Velda Johnston

Martin, a real estate broker gives a thumbnail sketch of Sag Harbor in this excerpt from Johnston's 1991 suspense novel, set in a village she calls Hampton Harbor. We recognize a reference to Metaphysical Books, an eclectic shop still in business. Johnston also pokes fun at the Sag Harbor Initiative which she refers to as the Hampton Harbor Symposium. —Ed.

Martin and I dined that night in the garden of a cafe near the Hampton Harbor waterfront. The last of the daylight mingled with the glow of the hurricane lamps on the tables. The cafe's exterior had struck me as extremely modest, but from the first bite I realized that the food rivaled that served by the posh Manhattan restaurants where Victor used to take me. The patrons, though, were not dressed like the ones I had seen at Lutèce. Like Martin, many of the men wore summerweight trousers and cotton turtlenecks. The women were equally casual in cotton dresses or pants and tops. I was glad I had chosen a yellow cotton sundress rather than the navy blue silk suit I had been tempted to wear.

Over our appetizer of artichoke hearts, I asked, "How long have you been in the real estate business?"

"I haven't been. I mean, I'm not now. I'm just holding the fort until my cousin recovers from a bad accident"

"A car crash?"

"Plane. An old Piper Cub he'd been flying for about ten years."

"And you can do that? Just leave your own work to take over your cousin's business?"

"Teachers don't work during the summer."

"Teachers!"

He smiled at my astonishment. "I teach English at Ardsmith College."

"I've heard of it. It's part of the state university system, isn't it?"

He nodded. "It's in Rockland County."

"I was an English major in college."

"Who wasn't?"

"You like teaching?"

"I love it,"

"And real estate?"

"It's not too bad, not for just the summer. And I like Hampton Harbor. I have ever since I spent summers here as a kid with my aunt and uncle and my cousins. It's such a maverick of a town, so different from the other Hamptons. In fact, it's called the un-Hampton Hampton."

I nodded. That day I'd seen two bicyclists wearing tee shirts with the printed slogan, "Hampton Harbor, the un-Hampton Hampton."

"It's the people who have always made it different," he went on. "The overwhelming majority of farmers and shopkeepers who settled other Hampton villages were of English ancestry. The whaleship owners and captains here in the Harbor were a pretty Waspy lot too. But the crews were polyglot, not just Yankees but Portuguese, Spaniards, American Indians, and even Fiji Islanders. Very early the Harbor developed a split personality. Musicales and champagne and crystal chandeliers in those mansions along Captains' Row — Do you know where that is?

"I think so. It's made up of those beautiful big houses on the residential part of Main Street, isn't it?"

He nodded, "By contrast, the part of town where we are now was wide open. More brothels and grog shops here than in all the rest of eastern Long Island."

"But that was long ago. How about later?"

"The town became even more of a mix. After whaling died out, a watch factory and various small industries tried to replace it. Polish and Italian and Irish immigrants came here to find work. Where once the town was Protestant, it became eighty percent Catholic. Then, about twenty-five years ago, well-off New Yorkers discovered that the Harbor had more fine old houses, many falling into decay, than any other village on eastern Long Island."

"Why more old houses here?"

"Bad times. Ever since whaling collapsed around 1850, the town had been in a depression. There wasn't enough money to tear down those old Colonial and Greek Revival houses and build something up-to-date in their place. The well-heeled New Yorkers bought up the old houses and restored them."

The Chablis Martin had ordered arrived at our table. I watched silently as the waiter went through the ritual of pouring a little wine for Martin to taste, and then filling both our glasses.

When the waiter had gone I said, "And who came after the rich New Yorkers?"

"The intellectuals. Writers, mostly. Each fall they hold something called the Hampton Harbor Symposium. They mull over the state of the world. Then they invite the populace to sit in the high school auditorium while they, seated on the stage, tell us what should be done about AIDS, crime, drugs, and such. The Symposium people tend to be leftish, and most of the natives in this village vote Republican, and so next year everyone expects that there'll be a beef about their using the words Hampton Harbor in the name for their get-together."

I smiled, "Any other new additions to the Harbor mix?"

"Yes. A revival of the sixties sensibility. Rolfing, and est, and all that. There's a shop in town that sells books on everything from astrology to witchcraft. It sells certain paraphernalia too. I see people of all ages going around the streets with crystal pendants dangling from around their necks. The crystals are to ward off evil vibes, or attract good ones, or something like that."

"And do they? What do you think about it?"

He shrugged, "It's a religion. I suppose, like any other religion, it works for you if you have faith in it. I never could have."

from Algren in Exile

Joe Pintauro

… Relatively alone, impoverished and unacclaimed, Algren kept up a front of armor, often employing the device of anticipatory attack. But just as often, he'd handle real insults with a mysterious poise. I began to worry about him in the Hamptons. He would be vulnerable here. Suddenly I appreciated how Algren — the man who had claimed for himself the words of Whitman: "I feel I am of them — I belong to those convicts and prostitutes myself" — could arouse the latent sadism of the kind of book reviewers who think fiction should abound in characters with whom they can identify, the kind of reviewers who really are defending themselves from existential insult. Nelson's discomfort among such literary types was the same discomfort he came to feel with the surrounding "Hamptons set." When he was with any of these people his arrogance would intensify as he strained for deeper, more outrageous responses. One night, at a crowded dinner table, he took out his dental bridge, washed it in his glass of water, and put it back in his mouth. And when Jessie Porter, his elderly next-door neighbor, complained to Nelson about how he neglected his house, Nelson, who customarily roamed about the house in a bathrobe, responded by flashing her the next time he caught her peering in his window. The Hamptons backed him, together with the whores and outcasts of his fiction, into an ideological corner.

Every day Nelson wore the same clothing: baggy trousers, high-top sneakers laced halfway, an occasional change of shirt — but in Sag Harbor this could be considered stylish. Often called the Un-Hampton, Sag Harbor is much like Key West, full of artists, writers, and editors, some with blue-collar incomes who blend in with the locals. Someone who fixes refrigerators might be a former executive of NBC, his customer a former executive of CBS. There are whalers' descendants, too, people whose ancestors arrived in the 1600s.

Canio Pavone's bookstore was just opening around the corner from Glover, a few yards from Nelson's front door, and one Saturday morning he sloshed in there in slippers. Canio was sweeping ancient dust out of the place. Here was someone even newer than Nelson.

"What the hell you tryin' to achieve here?" Nelson asked.

"I'm trying to open a bookstore." Canio has the good looks of a 1930s tango dancer, smiles shyly, and is inexhaustibly polite.

"Bookstore?" Nelson roared. "Hell, I got more books on my damn bed table."

Nelson returned with armloads of books for Canio. He visited the store every Saturday morning and it became the Nelson Algren Saturday Salon. Canio acquired an old sixties swivel armchair of green tweed from which Nelson loved to hold forth. A small group grew around that chair, which, to this day, remains the seat of honor at Canio's readings. Nelson turned the place into a hangout in a matter of weeks. There the storyteller sharpened his powers, dousing his groupies with a waterfall of jokes, gossip, advice. The lizardy, brownish rubbery skin around Nelson's eyes was blending with his deepening tan.

He got his old bike out of storage and though he and the bike made a clumsy couple, he managed to wave to friends as he weaved and bounced all around town.

By October, he was looking younger. In spite of his limited income, he insisted on picking up the tab for our regular lunches so vehemently sometimes that I'd be afraid it would end in a fistfight. We sat at "his" table next to the woodburning stove, where he could stare at the bay. "Jesus, was I

Canio's Books after a reading

wrong about Sag Harbor," he said. "This is, finally, home. I would've hated Southampton. Here I eat and watch water." He laughed softly. "For years I had this flash forward of myself eating and looking out at miles of water. Really. I swear." There was resignation in his voice as he gazed beyond the stacked rowboats to the people fishing on the bridge.

He stood up and introduced me to Johnny Ward, who owned the Bridge-view Diner. I had known John at a distance for more than 15 years. He ran for mayor a couple of times. But Nelson had, in less than a year, developed relationships with the working people of Sag Harbor that I hadn't in 15. Nelson went beyond knowing them. He transformed them, magically, into more vocal, vivid versions of themselves, acting in a drama that was really Nelson's own. He accomplished this by the intensely sophisticated art of listening. He shaped them by becoming their witness, and they knew he had the power to put them on the map.

"Did you see what Johnny has?" Nelson asked me.

"No. What?" I asked. He signaled and Johnny came up with a box of old

David Cummings and Bart

photos. He spread them out on the bar of that huge, failing restaurant and spoke proudly as he displayed his visions from the past: whaling photos, photos of old Sag Harbor. The town was barely recognizable. Nelson had seen and heard it all months before.

Algren had been consciously using Sag Harbor to frame an end for his career, a homey, low-budget retirement after a willfully lived, barely rewarded, though not unrecognized, life. Ironically for a man so closely identified with Chicago, Nelson Algren's bitterness found its balm here in Sag Harbor. Algren once said: "You can belong to New Orleans. You can belong to Boston or San Francisco. You might conceivably — however clandestinely — belong to Philadelphia. But you can't belong to Chicago any more than you can belong to a flying saucer called Los Angeles. For it isn't so much a city as it is a drafty hustler's junction in which to hustle a while and move on out of the draft."…

In Paris in the late forties and early fifties Algren's writing was being heralded. In Chicago, the critics were dumping on it. Algren headed for Europe, where he sojourned in Paris with Simone de Beauvoir while Sartre translated his Chicago: *City on the Make* and *Never Come Morning*. There Nelson also met James Jones, author of *From Here to Eternity*, and his wife, Gloria Mosolino. Years later, in the early seventies, Jim and Gloria gave up Paris and moved to a house on a hill in the Hamptons, complete with grape arbor and acres of potato fields. Jim died in May of 1977, but Gloria carried on their tradition of hospitality as the pre-eminent hostess to friends, writers, and artists, including Heller, Knowles, Styron, Shaw, and Puzo.

Nelson hadn't seen Gloria since Paris and he called her up. Gloria introduced Nelson to a world that exemplifies but transcends, the cliche of the Hamptons. He met old confreres like Kurt Vonnegut, whom he had known at the University of Iowa. Vonnegut took Nelson to dinner at the American Hotel and introduced him to John Irving. "But Nelson's wisecracks to Irving that night didn't make sense," Vonnegut says. "The whole night Nelson thought he was with Clifford Irving." Candida Donadio, Nelson's agent, put him in touch with Peter Matthiessen. Peter and his wife, Maria, welcomed Nelson to dinners and Nelson returned the gesture. It was as if a nucleus of his past and the beginnings of a future had been waiting for him all along, here at the tip of Long Island.

One day some 18 of us received this invitation:

DRINKS AFTER FIVE

DINNER AT SEVEN

THURSDAY, DECEMBER EIGHTEEN, 1980

HOME OF NELSON ALGREN

Nelson had pounded more nails into the walls and strung up old-fashioned outdoor Christmas lights. The ceilings radiated with bursts of red, yellow, and green. Walking inside the house was like penetrating cubicles of punk art in some awful East Village gallery. The extra-large Christmas lights had been in one of the boxes that had trailed after him all the years. Nelson kept

things, from his old bike to his Christmas lights, carrying them with him his whole life, as if they were props and he were a kind of one-man theatre. There was a high purpose to this junk that had repelled the would-be land-lady in Southampton.

He introduced me to Canio first, then to his close friend Roy Finer, a detective who looked as if he had stepped out of a 1940s film noir. The small house seemed crowded with people who were delicately stepping around piles of books and unidentifiable artifacts, trying not to topple their glasses. For tablecloths, the small table in the living room was spread with the bath-room curtains. Finally, as we drank his excellent champagne, Nelson emerged from the kitchen with a sliced ham, aluminum trays of ziti, and huge plastic containers of ambrosia, all from Hans's Deli, and directed every-body to fill his plate. At the same time he was flinging seating orders at his guests, separating us into two groups, one in the dining room and the other in the living room. In the confusion it appeared that he had forgotten about Gloria Jones, who floated between rooms. I stood up, lifting my chair.

"Gloria, sit here," I called. Nelson froze and glared at me.

"Stay where the hell I put you." He was hyperventilating.

"I think Gloria needs a chair," I said.

"You don't know everything. Now, just sit down. I said sit."

Gloria threw me a cautionary glance and I sat, glowering and embarrassed, thinking my dish of ziti on his walls might complement the decor.

He pulled two chairs to the middle of the floor, dragged a gray metal typewriter table away from the wall, opened its flaps, and gestured gallantly for Gloria to sit down. She sat with a smile as he lifted a bottle of liquor. He turned to me.

"Now," he said, taking a relaxed breath, "I want to toast a friend, who is present. Joe." He winked at me and smiled. "This is in honor of you, the man who put an end to my losing streak."

"Hear, hear!" they chanted. I swallowed my anger and drowned my misgivings in his wonderful champagne.

Early that winter of 1981, Nelson had been notified of his election to the American Academy and Institute of Arts and Letters. He was to be inducted on May 20th. This exploded the cozy picture of his exile. He had received a literary award as early as 1947, but generally speaking, no greater literary distinction is available in the United States than to be elected and inducted into the academy. Sometime in the 1970s Kurt Vonnegut had put Nelson up for a medal of merit at the academy. "I read the citation," Kurt explained, "but he never showed up. My first words that day were: 'It's very much in character for the recipient of this medal not to be here.' I later telephoned him and said, 'Come get your medal. I think it's gold.' You know what his response was? 'Mail it to me.' I was under the mistaken impression," Vonnegut went on, "that these medals were made of gold, you know, worth $3,000 or so, and therefore highly hockable to say the least. But a medal from the academy is not election to the academy and I think it only insulted him. Sometime later I asked Nelson what had happened to the medal. 'You know it's worth money,' I said. 'I dunno,' he answered, 'it must've rolled under the couch.'"

While Nelson publicly pooh-poohed election to the academy, when it was offered in 1981 it satisfied him deeply. He stopped falling into those dark panics in which he would declaim, bitterly, as if addressing a jury seated somewhere above his head: "I'm on a blacklist. I don't know who put me on it, but it's American. The Germans read me and buy me. They can't get enough of me. In my own country they treat me like shit." Now he was saying: "This is the turnaround. Publishers will notice. Money will start coming in."

Our lunches were no longer at the Bridgeview Diner. Now he was taking me to the fancy Cato's in Bridgehampton. He gave me a copy of *The Last Carousel* and inscribed it with the words of his toast: "For Joe, the man who put an end to my losing streak." Everything he had mourned as lost seemed on the brink of coming back to him. It was as if he had forgotten about luck, given up too soon on the goodness of the world and its possibilities. Now he was adjusting to his new good fortune, acting more irreverent than ever, but this time with great style. His energy and his confidence soared. Not only was he now a star; he realized that he had always been one. His habitual low-grade depression was gone, and one could see through the old man, as through a newly cleaned window, to the hot-blooded hustler, the lean and hungry wolf, back on the make....

Nelson suddenly became the dashing raconteur, a confident actor swinging both arms behind fancy couches like a bird unfolding, crossing his legs and bubbling cleverly forth at center stage with oversize gestures. The swaggering American in Paris had been resurrected. At parties he and Gloria were uninterruptible, hysterically funny together, spilling over with stories. Still, he kept faith with his cronies and worshipers at Canio's on Saturdays.

As if Nelson had all along been someone else, the news broke that a literary giant had emerged from obscurity in the Hamptons. His telephone number was unlisted and people turned to me in search of him. Reporters for *The New York Times* and *Newsday*, called unceasingly for help in arranging interviews. Betty Friedan, as well as several old Chicago acquaintances who had settled in East Hampton, was in desperate pursuit of Nelson, but he refused to allow me to give out his number, grumbling about the rich and famous. More than once Nelson asked me not to oblige any of them. I never questioned whether this resurgence of his celebrity was for the best. It satisfied him. But it was also agitating him.

After the high, his bitterness started to resurface. He wanted payment for those bad years. He lashed out at those who had scoffed, took his revenge for past injustices, as he reconstructed the earlier chapters of his life to fit this new twist in the plot. At the same time he looked more kindly upon his neighbors, realizing that they were not uniformly snobs or gangs of vapid rich. Betty Friedan drove a $100 wreck. Next time she called I simply told her: "Look out your window. He lives across the street from you." Friedan reconnected Nelson to his old Chicago buddies, and he and Betty became good friends.

He asked Gloria to accompany him to his May 20th induction at the academy and started making plans for an elegant lawn party in honor of a Chicago journalist friend of his, to take place at Nelson's house on May ninth. He asked me to come by early to help him greet people.

That morning I dressed in white and walked to Nelson's house. As I approached, I saw a small man crouching and snapping off photos of the house. Yellow-faced and sweating, he lowered his camera as I came up to him.

"Do you know Nelson? What's your name?" he panted.

"Who are you?" I asked indignantly.

"I'm doing my job. I'm a reporter." He fished for a press card. "May I take your picture?"

"No. If you don't mind. Is anything wrong? What's wrong?"

"He's dead. Nelson is dead." The man seemed terrified, poised with his camera.

"Wait a minute...."

"Where does Betty Friedan live?" he asked breathlessly. "I understand she lives nearby."

"Who are you?"

"I'm a friend of Nelson's. I'm legit. Look, I'm a little nervous." He was wildly distraught. "Sorry. It was for me, this party."

"Who's with Nelson? Where…?"

"In the bathroom. On the floor. You know his friend Roy? Roy cut open the screen door and forced his way into the house. I'm a friend…. I just don't know what else to do…. I'm a journalist. Where's Friedan's house?" he repeated. I pointed to it across the street. He ran toward it and I turned to see Roy coming out of the house, gray-faced, shaking his head.

"His heart," Roy said. "He's on the floor in the bathroom. It's not pretty."

"Are you sure he's dead?"

"He's dead. He'd had heart trouble before coming here, a heart attack a couple of years back."

"He what?… He never told me that."

"You don't want to go in, Joe."

"When did this happen?"

"His wrist watch smashed against the tub or something. The hands are stuck at 6:05, so I figure this morning at 6:05."

"Roy… What do we do? Guests will be showing up."

"Go home. I'll wait for the police."

"But you don't look well." Roy had recently had an operation. He looked exhausted.

"You don't look so good yourself," he said. "Go home. Police'll turn the guests away. I'll hang around till they get here and catch up to you, unless maybe… I'll just take the train back."

Unknown to me, earlier in the week Nelson had had chest pains and had visited a doctor on Main Street. The doctor had urged him to go to Southampton Hospital's emergency room, but Nelson, it seems, had left the doctor's office with no intention of doing that. He had a party to pull off Saturday.

At home, waiting for Roy to call, I pictured the guests being turned away. Roy finally called to say that the local police were with Nelson's body and that he was taking the train back. I assumed that I would hear about Nelson's

Oakland Cemetery

funeral arrangements before the end of the day, but by nightfall my phone hadn't rung.

All that night the dogs in my house couldn't sleep. They paced around my bed; then, about two in the morning, they sprang up and ran downstairs wagging their tails as if someone had come to the front door. I couldn't shake the silly thought that Nelson's ghost had walked into my house. So real was the feeling that mentally I greeted him, letting him know he was safe and welcome. As I lay in bed, I imagined Nelson in the wicker chair on the porch, enjoying the moonlight. For the rest of the night, the dogs slept downstairs.

Sitting for Mike

Canio Pavone

Mona Lisa sat for Leonardo, Gertrude Stein sat for Pablo, and I sat for Mike. I still feel the lightness in my head and the rush of blood through my body that day when Mike came into the bookshop. He hesitated for a moment, eyes searching the floor, his tongue slipping thoughtfully over his lower lip. Finally he looked up directly into my eyes:

"Canio, I'd like to paint your portrait."

I was surprised, but answered without hesitation:

"Sure, Mike."

My easy smile betrayed the excitement I felt. He had chosen *me*. He had looked around and ultimately chosen *me*. It was the height of flattery.

I felt a little smug and simulated a cool countenance, but it was more like keeping down the lid of a whistling teakettle. Flying insects ricocheted off the walls of my stomach, and my heartbeat picked up the tempo.

I wondered if this was what my wife felt when I proposed to her three decades earlier, the thrill of being the object of someone's attention, the focus of his eye, the dead center of his target. She, too, gave me an easy smile, and seemed unperturbed. The darkness of the evening in that distant South American garden was a convenient cover for *my* nervousness, a nervousness prompted by the idea of a possible rejection. I wondered if this was what Mike was feeling when he asked me to sit for him. It was to be an intimate affair, after all… he, perusing my features purposefully, learning who dwelt

Canio Pavone celebrates 20 years at the shop

behind the facade, and I, accommodating him as best I could, turning slightly toward the window, chin higher, trying not to move.

"It will have to be early, Mike. I ought to be back in Sag Harbor to open the shop at noon."

He needed only a couple of hours. We would start at 9 a.m.

Those days I still slept on a cot in the rear of the shop among the used non-fiction. It had only been a few years since I had opened the small shop of used books, but already it was known for miles around because of the weekly poetry readings, book signings, music events and art shows, all of which serviced local talent but soon attracted writers and artists from as far away as Manhattan. Helen Harrison, art critic of *The New York Times*, had reviewed the first art show, paintings of Karen Yamaguchi, and that helped put the gallery–bookshop on the cultural map of Long Island. I eventually got to know the big, bearded man who attended all the openings with his wife and four children: Mike Loos, a tool and dye maker who devoted weekends and evenings to painting. He sold some of his work at the art fairs on the Long Wharf in Sag Harbor or at art shows in nearby malls. His first exhibition, however, was at Canio's Books, and it made him feel validated as an artist,

enough to rent a studio space in Riverhead, some twenty miles from home.

Although my cot was behind a big bookcase, several aisles up from the poetry section, it wasn't so far that I couldn't hear voices at night — Longfellow, Whitman, Dickinson, Lorca, Dante. Whatever deprivations I suffered at the time, I never felt lonely. Words floated out to me from the hardbound volumes:

"This is the forest primeval, the murmuring pines and the hemlocks…"

"O Captain, O Captain, our fearful trip is done…"

"This is my letter to the world that never wrote to me…"

By six a.m. the sun was already in my eyes, and sitting for Mike was at the top of my agenda. I rolled towards Riverhead, cutting through the dusty farm roads of Water Mill, along the dreamy Peconic waters of Southampton, straight down dull Route 27 to Route 24 North, past the Big Duck and the defunct gas stations of Flanders into the downtrodden downtown of Riverhead.

This was the year of the *Salon des Réfusés*. The Parrish Art Museum held a juried show, and profoundly offended local artists by exhibiting a mere handful of the entries, and rejecting the great majority. Mike's work was among the chosen few, but he nevertheless joined the picket line of artists, led by Nathan Kuhn, who protested the curator's manner of selection. To counter the museum's elitist attitude, another exhibit, a *salon des refuses*, was set up by Nathan in a big empty building in downtown Riverhead. The statement was made, but Riverhead was not the Hamptons, so the effect was minimal.

Mike's sympathy for the rejected didn't prevent him and his family and a host of friends from attending the opening night at the Parrish. Cameras clicked all evening as the beautiful people of the Hamptons art scene paraded through the museum. We passed the portrait of Andy Warhol painted on velour by Julian Schnabel.

"What dreck!" someone behind us muttered. Was that a reflection on the sitter or the painter? I wondered. We stepped up into the larger room in back to view Bob Giard's elegant photographic portrait of Joe Pintauro. The lush, sensuous quality, the warmth… was that an emanation of Pintauro, the sitter, or Giard, the photographer?

Then we saw it, next to the staircase: Mike's painting of some local firemen, their heads out of the picture, their hands comfortably cradling their crotches. We stood there admiring, and embraced our beaming Mike.

The sounds and sights of that resplendent evening still reverberated many days later as I climbed the stairs of that Riverhead building to Mike's studio. The pungent smell of oil paints and acrylics permeated the entire place, where many artist studios were installed. Halfway up I met Mike, who was coming down to meet me. We passed Nathan's studio, and I still remember his cut-out painting/sculpture of a large yellow banana. Up we continued.

Mike's studio was an open space with tall dusty windows, paintings and frames leaning against the walls, and an easel set up in the center of the room. I sat on a chair and he perched upon a stool in front of the easel, setting right to work with pastels in hand. I felt his eyes pierce every part of my face while his fingers ran up and down the paper.

"Talk to me, but don't move," he commanded.

So I complained about my run-in with the over-zealous state police on Route 27. Imagine, giving me a ticket during a snowstorm for not signaling when changing lanes. And no one else on the road! And another time for speeding, a bit more than 65 mph.

"Hold it. Don't move. Smile naturally."

Mike was clearly concentrating on something other than my police sto-

ries. I worried how my receding hairline would look in the painting, and what Mike would do with my hands. Shouldn't I be holding a book, after all?

"I almost have it," Mike said after an hour during which his hands never stopped moving, dabbing, smearing, scratching, pushing, working the pastels from all sides. Just when I guessed we were finished, he said:

"OK, let's have a break."

I couldn't understand what was taking him so long. How many strokes were needed to represent me? In a short time we resumed the task. He studied me and I studied him.

How would *I* paint *his* portrait? Which characteristics would I try to capture? The yellow–brown hair growing over his ears? The full red lips engulfed in his grizzly beard? The pinhole eyes darting in many directions behind the glasses which he constantly pushed up with index finger as they slipped down with perspiration? His solid shoulders, the paunch holding up a majestic chest? The feet which moved with the grace of a leprechaun? How to capture that hearty laughter, beginning down in his abdomen, gathering force as it rose up through his throat and finally let loose like the bark of a seal? How to depict the sound of his voice, honey traveling slowly over smooth beach pebbles sprinkled with sand? How to tell of his intelligence and wit: a star outlasting storms, smiling on tides, soaring with ease through darkness?

The portrait appeared in his next show: *The Essence of Canio*, he called it. A large canvas, some three feet by four feet, with a full portrait of... my mouth! All right, my *smiling* mouth. No neck, no eyes, no ears, no receding hairline. My essence reduced to a smile.

Mike died, too young, from a massive heart attack a few years later while sitting on his surfboard talking to his young sons at Sagaponack Beach.

It has been pointed out that the woman smiling mysteriously in *La Gioconda* is as much Leonardo as she is Mona Lisa; we can all see the intensity of Picasso straining in the form of Gertrude Stein. I enter into my portrait and find Mike, gurgling in the vermilion, swirling in the magenta, and doing somersaults in the aquamarine.

Reveling in Tomatoes

Miriam Ungerer

The rest of the country celebrates the first Monday in September as Labor Day, but on the East End of Long Island, local people really can't celebrate much until the first Tuesday in September. It's the day when some small measure of peace and sanity returns after a summer of nerve-jangling chaos and traffic.

It's my favorite season of the year, when I can happily browse my most cherished farm stands once again.

Nature obliges with a continuum of fruits and vegetables that merge summer with autumn — there are tomatoes and eggplants, salads and herbs still thrive, and the late corn still stands in the fields.

But it is the unique flavor of voluptuous Long Island tomatoes that I will lament the most when their season is over. Fortunately, if the weather behaves itself, we sometimes have tomatoes until mid-October. Here are some ways to revel in the glut of tomatoes and don't forget to put some by — either by canning or freezing — for those drear days of winter when we are once again confronted with those vapid, hard, pink baseballs in the stores.

Since local field tomatoes can be bought vine-ripened at nearby farm-stands, there's no point in selecting under-ripe examples to line up on windowsills. As I've pointed out year after year, tomatoes don't like bright sunlight once they're picked and the hot windowsill does nothing but rot them.

Tomatoes are best kept in a single layer resting comfortably on a crushed-paper-towel-lined basket in a dim, airy spot. (During the recent unpleasant heat wave I kept my tomatoes — and peaches — in an air-conditioned bed-room; to some of us, they're almost as pretty as flowers.)

Like bananas, you should never put tomatoes in the refrigerator. No, no, no. They begin to die at temperatures below 60 degrees and in just a few hours lose most of their lusty flavor.

Unfortunately, vine-ripened tomatoes are a cantankerous lot, the best of them thin-skinned and sensitive to bruising and temperature. This is why you can never experience truly great tomatoes more than a few days away from their birthplace. (The same goes for peaches).

I've successfully shipped a few, heavily bubble-wrapped, by second-day air express to one of my tomato-loving daughters who lives in distant, tomato-hostile country. Personally, I can't see living in tomato exile, but some people will sacrifice almost anything for mountain views!

Even though it is technically possible to grow tomatoes in containers just about anywhere in the lower 48 (there are hundreds of varieties hybridized to grow in almost any climate), they never ever measure up to the taste of toma-toes raised in the sun and soil and salty air of the eastern end of Long Island. So take that, New Jersey!

If you grow your own tomatoes, there are about 100 things you need to know to meet with success — problems like blossom end rot, catfacing, sun-scald, cracking, early blight, late blight, blossom drop, and leaf spot. Then there are tomato predators like blister beetles, hornworms, fruitworms, stink bugs, and cutworms, to say nothing of deer and raccoons, which are vora-cious fanciers of tomatoes.

So thank your lucky stars for all the farmers hereabouts who worry about all these perils for you. I, masochistically, am growing a few vines of my own and learn of some new peril every season.

Did you know that nicotine can affect tomato plants? Never let anyone smoke in the garden (just in the house), as it can cause mosaic virus, a serious disease that can cut down on the harvest. And if you smoke, you must wash your hands with soap and water before fiddling around with your plants. Got this straight from the noted garden authorities Dick and Jan Raymond, authors of many informative books aimed at novice and veteran gardener alike.

So maybe you'd just rather take a run to your nearest farmstand.

Bruschetta

Although this Italian first course — grilled bread with something on top of it — has become commonplace in the past couple of years, it can range from being wonderful to being just soggy toast. Care must be taken with this simple dish. You must begin with a first-class Tuscan loaf of bread and perfect, vine-ripened tomatoes. In fact, every ingredient must be of the finest quality.

Serves four.

4 large slices round Tuscan white bread (no sourdough)

1 large fresh garlic clove, split

Extra-virgin olive oil

2 large, very ripe tomatoes, diced (by hand) and drained 5 minutes

1 Tbsp. finely chopped fresh rosemary, thyme, and parsley, mixed

Sea salt, medium grind to taste

Freshly milled black pepper to taste

More best quality olive oil

Cut the bread about half an inch thick and grill it. An outdoor charcoal grill is ideal; however, I've made this successfully on my gas stove's grill.

As soon as the toast is lightly golden and marked with grids, remove it and rub it well with the cut raw garlic, impaled on the tines of a fork. Brush with olive oil. Combine the tomatoes with the herbs and salt and pepper to taste, then pile the mixture onto the grilled bread.

Drizzle quickly with a bit more olive oil and serve pronto. Bruschetta gets soggy if it sits around.

Tomatoes Stuffed With Rice Salad and Crab

This is a fine entree for a late summer lunch. Most of the work can be done ahead and then assembled just before serving. It is best never to refrigerate tomatoes, so you cannot stuff them too much ahead of time. Also, rice is inedible after refrigeration unless it is re-hydrated by steaming.

Serves six
6 large ripe tomatoes
3 cups rice salad (recipe follows)
1 head curly oakleaf lettuce
Garnish: Calamata olives

Cut the tops off the tomatoes and scoop out the seeds and most of the interior. Place them upside down to drain. Just before serving, stuff them with the following rice and crab salad.

Rice and Crab Salad

2 cups cooked long grain rice
¼ cup parsley, minced
2 Tbsp. coriander or tarragon, minced
¼ cup red onion, minced
3 Tbsp. lemon juice
3 Tbsp. cold-pressed olive oil
1 tsp. salt
lots of freshly ground white pepper
1 cup fresh lump crabmeat

Allow the rice to cool to tepid before mixing it with all the remaining ingredients. Pick over the crabmeat (frequently there are some bits of cartilage lurking) and pull it into small pieces before mixing it with the rice. Fill the drained tomatoes with the rice salad and arrange each on a bed of curly pale green lettuce. Decorate with the olives.

Tomato and Basil Bread

I had this bread first many years ago at the Sunset Grill, a restaurant facing the water in Sag Harbor that, amazingly, is still there, although under a new name. I got nowhere with inquiries about its creator — only that his name was John, who is long gone from here — but I still make his bread. I had to make up my own recipe. You must skin a couple of big tomatoes, seed them, and puree them to get the fresh tomato pulp for this bread.

Makes two loaves
3 cups all-purpose flour (approx.)

1 pkg. dry yeast
1 cup fresh tomato puree
1 Tbsp. butter, softened
1 tsp. salt
½ cup fresh basil leaves, shredded

This is for the fast food processor technique. Those accustomed to baking bread will have no trouble adapting it to a handmade version. Use the steel blade in the processor.

Heat the tomato puree in a saucepan and stir in the salt and butter until the butter melts. Into the work bowl of the processor measure 1 cup of flour and the yeast. Pulse to blend thoroughly. With the machine running, pour the tomato puree through the feed tube. Then add more flour, ¼ cup at a time, until the dough becomes a solid mass that rides on the blade and cleans the sides of the bowl. Knead with the machine running for one minute.

If the dough is too dry, add a few drops of water; if too wet, sprinkle in a tablespoon or so of flour. This is a rather sticky dough.

Remove the dough from the work bowl, work in the basil, and knead it lightly on a floured board by hand for a minute or two. Put it into a greased bowl, cover with plastic wrap, and let rise until doubled in bulk, about one hour.

Punch down the dough and divide it into two balls. On a floured surface, roll each ball into a cylinder about 18 inches long. Place these, not touching, on a baking sheet lined with parchment baking paper. Let rise for about 45 minutes, or until double in size. Do not let them over-rise or they will collapse in the heat of the oven.

Preheat the oven to 375 degrees. Bake the loaves on the center rack for about 30 minutes, until they will yield a hollow sound when tapped on the bottom. Cool to tepid before slicing. Serve with a fruity, dark green olive oil for dipping.

Mapping Sag Harbor

Carol Williams

When one of my sons was looking for his own low-rent apartment in Sag Harbor, he ran into Jim Turner in the bank. "Spend a couple of hours walking up and down Main Street," Jim advised. "You can get anything you could ever want that way."

I think that is true; it is something about the map. I know a bit about the map of Sag Harbor, because I made it. And that came about exactly as Jim said.

Like my son twenty-five years later, I was just out of college and looking for a cheap place to live. Not being real-estate office material, I asked in the deli on Main Street. Both the man making the sandwich and the woman waiting told me to "Ask Rocco." They pointed out his shop, diagonally across Main Street, just past the fork. I found Rocco Liccardi feeding goats near the reedy spot in his backyard. "Funny," he said. "No matter what I bring them, they always prefer the bag."

Rocco didn't know of anywhere I could live. But he said I should meet Nancy Willey so we left the goats chewing brown paper, fresh greens scattered around their hooves. Nancy lived in a small, long-roofed, low-porched house, three doors up, which we reached across the intervening disheveled backyards. She had white hair, was deceptively slight and made tea. We drank it by her ancient fireplace, while she told me about building a house with Frank Lloyd Wright. Then she made me a deal: a room in her brother's house (attached to one of the yards Rocco and I had just trespassed across) in

Rocco's Antiques

exchange for my becoming recording secretary of the newly formed Sag Harbor Planning Board.

The map came up when the board discovered that it couldn't plan without a proper map. They were going to hire an engineer to create one when, without thinking, I looked up from the minutes to volunteer. "I can make a map," I said, which was of course completely insane. But I needed the money, and more than that, I wanted to map Sag Harbor.

By luck, it turned out I could do it. The Suffolk County government was in the process of making an aerial survey of the county and had the projected (to compensate for curvature of the earth) outlines of what could be almost anything on large pieces of paper. Generously, their planners gave me the Sag Harbor sheets. That was just the beginning. For months I walked and rode my bicycle through back streets and main streets, down alleys, across bridges, along coves, around ponds, creeks, and park, reconciling outlines with reality, the map with the territory. I became familiar with the contents of everyone's washing lines, which way the seagulls face in what winds, how many spiderworts grow between the paving stones. Finally, rapidograph in hand, I transferred every curve and interstice of what I had seen onto a final Mylar. It was as though I had traced a spider-web: as perfect and as alive.

And, like a fly in that web, I got stuck here. Many people do: they think it's the quaint houses or the harbor or the convenient distance to the City, and maybe it is all that too. But beneath and beyond any part of the village, it has to be the web: the mesmerizing pattern of our streets. Our three broad streets become roads that link us, beyond village boundaries and through the woods, to the ocean and to a larger town with more movies. Slung between these branches are the labyrinthine side streets and alley ways that diverge to wrap around ponds, coves, schools, and graveyards. And everything converges at last in the single curving Main Street, which inevitably connects us to each other, and which, in turn, funnels onto Long Wharf that leads straight out to sea and vast expanses of sky. With such a map, every errand is an adventure, every encounter a potentially changed life.

A Wonderful Place to Write

Arthur Prager

On a Spring day in 1963 a friend invited me to spend a weekend at her house in Sag Harbor. This was not unexpected. She had invited me many times before. I declined as usual, citing "other plans." The real reason was that I thought Sag Harbor was in Maine.

She kept asking, and in due course the penny dropped and I accepted. As I crossed Brick Kiln Road into Main Street my life changed. I fell in love, not, alas, with my generous hostess but with the village. By Monday morning I had found a real estate broker and sent him off to find the elusive combination of what I wanted (perfection) and what I could afford ($6,000). It took three years. I began a new incarnation as a Man of Property.

"The land, Scarlett! The land," as Mr. O'Hara said. The land was all right, but the house was a disaster. Inside were broken plaster walls with dirty lath peeping through, paneless windows, a general air of poverty and hopelessness. Outside, a saddle-back roof and what must certainly have been the original cracked, stained shingles. I couldn't afford architects and contractors, so I worked on it myself on weekends.

Little by little I created a viable living room and a clean, comfortable bedroom with the help of the Nilssen brothers, proprietors of the great junk and second-hand everything barn in Southampton. The East Hampton Bargain Box provided a touch of gentility. In time my house would rise to the "fishing shack" category, and I could call it "my place in the Hamptons."

131

Among friends I called it "geek revival," but in 1973 the picture changed. Robert H. Pine issued his planning study, *Sag Harbor: Past, Present and Future*, and I discovered that what I owned was a colonial "half-house" built in 1730, a rare and valuable antique and one of the oldest houses in the village. I also discovered that it was an ideal place for writing, quiet, uncomplicated and best of all, cheap. Somehow, as it always does, the word got around. My telephone began to ring. I was besieged by writers, some of whom I had never met, asking if it was available for a week, two weeks, all summer? Because of its Spartan simplicity, I couldn't charge very much rent, and that got around too.

What made it so desirable to writers? That is a mystery, although I have heard the word "charm" applied from time to time. I think its total lack of pretense was a strong factor. I had furnished it so that two or three sandy children and a wet dog could come in from the beach at any time and no one would say a word. Writers could put their feet on the furniture, smoke cigars, leave dirty dishes in the sink. I had put in an Oxford English Dictionary, and a thesaurus. It was within walking distance of the grocery and the liquor store. But the big drawing card was the price. It was a bargain, and serious writers love a bargain (if Dr. Samuel Johnson didn't say that, he should have).

I had written *Rascals at Large* and *The Mahogany Tree* there. My daughter Emily had done pieces for the *National Lampoon* and her first fiction, *A Visit from the Footbinder* and *Clea and Zeus Divorce* in the upstairs bedroom. Now outsiders, some of whom were just beginning their writing careers, came along. I had made my garage into a kind of studio, and there Thomas Harris wrote *Red Dragon*, making it the birthplace of the redoubtable Dr. Hannibal Lecter. Tom also told me that the studio had served as the model for the bedroom in which his serial killer, Francis Dolarhyde, who bit off people's lips with his grandmother's false teeth, planned his outrageous crimes.

The late Willard Espy, wordsmith, essayist and light versifier wrote *Have a Word on Me* in the garden on a makeshift table made of two sawhorses and an old door. Liberal pundit Al Franken and Tom Davis, then writing for Saturday Night Live, would escape from their womenfolk for a week or two and move into my living room to try to find out what made Americans laugh. The result was The Coneheads and other classic SNL bits. Mary Breasted, front page reporter of *The New York Times* wrote her first novel, *I Shouldn't Be Telling You This* on my dining room table. Food critic Seymour Britchky wrote *The Lutèce Cookbook*, testing the four-star recipes in my six-by-four Nilssen-furnished kitchen.

Whaling Museum, Main Street

To counteract the rich aroma of French haute cuisine, young Lorraine Dusky wrote a diet book, *How to Eat Like a Thin Person*, using the same kitchen. The late Bill Cardoso, who coined the term "gonzo" for a certain type of journalist, sprawled on my couch wrangling with agents and editors on my telephone (the phone company wouldn't give him one), and blocked out what would later become his next and last book, *The Maltese Sangweech*. He was then working as a dishwasher at the American Hotel.

They came and they went. Some achieved national and even international fame. Some were never heard of again. The great and the near great no longer want my house, which is no longer at the fishing shack level and is certainly no longer a bargain. Poor writers have found other places in which to write. Sag Harbor, like Bloomsbury and the left bank of Paris, has become expensive, but it's still a wonderful place to write.

My Village Under a Northeaster

Allen Planz

Driven wild, nunbouys spindle in the rip.
Hogchokers flop on shore, nearly airborne
on bladderwort and sputnik weed still bearing rock.
Spoondrift raze riprap where no one walks
but one gull drunk from riding updrafts.

In the fishing station our hearts pump piss.
McLane curses the weather that whiskey
raises with the wind and the dead.
Baymen, not daring breakwater, pass the bottle
and make jokes about wops and widows,
though thinking of fair seas and fair women,
Everything that's foul steams in raingear
and driven wiggy, we crack up laughing.

O Danny McLane, O Mayor Ward,
that big bass I caught under the bridge
tasted of municipal sewage
even though it got a picture in the paper
to support the dredging boondoggle.
Loving this land, we can lie for it.

Call it love, or pride, pride!
Rain falls while shit flies!
Our teenagers run away to the city
where they make love all day and hair
grows like Asia on their bodies.
The tourists skip the Legion parade,
shoplift the docks, shagass elsewhere.

But Steinbeck's dead, who once joked here
and taught the boys to grow beards in spring
to show they're whalemen still.
Freshly shaven, they await the draft
or crewing a construction team.

Pass the bottle: a swig for kids
wasted all over hell and gone.
But now I remember the pain
when I called you nogood sonovabitch
for what you wrote of Vietnam
and McLane and the Baymen swayed into silence
and you started talking of your death,
so soon to come, and of mine, scare
dividing flesh from flesh, village
from nation. Where's the guys who'd rather
fish than drink, John? Where the hell's
California
when widows and whalemen face the sea?

Algonquin Morning Song

Vince Clemente

Early morning
 walking the treeline
  along Otter Pond,

I chant vespers,
 prayerful, in the old
  Algonquin tongue:

Nissequogue
 Peconic
  Connetquot,

wake the river gods
 sleeping, in the leaning
  shore reeds.

Peninsula

Vince Clemente

This is all there is between us and oblivion,
neck-road over the inlet to Redwood:
to swerve would mean to tumble
into the water, always that close.

I'm sure there are stories of those
who come back as dolphins, or starfish,
back from depths of zero-light with news,
a mote on our radar screen, infinitesimal as dew

As good as it gets: leavening our days,
the garvey rocking in the tide-swell;

an age'd man drops his line, stares
into a froth of nebulae, prays

to a listening God.

Cricket at a Poetry Reading

Vince Clemente

The cricket sang
the poet turned a line
then another, high above
the cricket's undersong.

To think that such a thing,
(my, it had its nerve)
would dare trill, no matter
how softly, as poets sing.

Be it blessing or curse,
I can't decide — can you, yet
in a single insect's voice, listen:
the song-weary universe.

(for Canio Pavone)

4:30 A.M. Noyac Bay

Terence M. Sullivan

The bay a well
waxed shell
a military floor
      deep sheen.

The swell humps
      and small bumps
of bluefish
quietly devouring
      their own.
They break fast
      in numbers
the execution
of dawn's hum.

Fullish Moon Lighting

Terence M. Sullivan

The fullish moon and I conspired
she icing the tidal
      flow
highlighting rising fins
for me to fish to.

Her white blue glow through the trees
rising the pond folds and rolls
to three dimensional relief
backlighting the striped bass head

striking his prey on my line
thrashing showers of moonbeams
rain upside down
tail cut crystal spray.

Celebrating this sacrament
that will turn
to extreme unction
as the bass lies curled
in the cooler
going home.

August dusk: Sag Harbor.

R. B. Weber

Sutures of shadows lace the grass,
while across the street   some small   crazy
legged children   run around   and
around   playing   Indians   while
(woowoo, woowoo, woowoo, woowoo)
a robin sits on a branch above
preening the lice from its softfeather
breast   The small pumping legs
continue to run   bright   red
feathers   in shuttles from trees
to garden   and back again   until
a porch light   blinks on   a voice
and the robin   plummets a last flash.

Descent

Star Black

The bookish exhaustion of September's trees —
they are overstudious and soon will freeze.
Their leaves will painfully fall asleep
perjured by Persephone who refuses to leave.

She does, but not before dithering in skirts of rust,
dusting pavements unnecessarily as if she must
tidy up her desultory hesitations before her lust,
like cool fire, plausive and persuadable, thrusts

her toward the famished excavations below,
their doleful monotones waiting in parched snow,
their periscopes nudging each green plumule

as it begins to grow back through plinths of stone,
each teeny pinnacle of somnolent hope. Never alone,
she curls and moans, summer's but her second home.

Traffic

Star Black

Back to work, everyone's going back to work,
except the service industry that works for those
away from work and the unemployed without work
and the laid-off looking for work who were looking

for work all along and the ailing who can't work.
Otherwise, everyone's going back to work. Trees,
solemn chaperons with sober leaves, lean toward
the direction of salaries. The sky, invigorated by

cyclic patterns of society, sprawls quietly like
a schoolmarm's daydream of sex with a stranger
who has a patch over one eye. Fast cars, purposeful
preludes to frost, rush across stern intersections.

Chromosomes coil and burst. Summer's a dumpster
of irretrievables. Tourism's over, the freeways taut.

Osprey

George Held

Osprey, you can see by the dawn's
        Early light
A fish 'neath the finish of the bay
        In your flight
As you circle and soar or you stall
        Like a kite,
Ever ready to dive on your prey
        When in sight;
Then you drop like a plummet until
        You alight
On the brine with your talons outstretched
        And they bite
Into scales of that silvery bass, lifting it clear
        Of the bight
Of the bay with your ten-horse wings to retake
        The sun's light,
And you land on your platform to tend to your
                        nestling's
        End of night
Hunger, tearing the bass with your terrible beak
        Into bite-
Sized gobbets for your fledgling to gorge on,
                        its break-
        Fast birthright
As your scion, O Osprey, you long-wingéd king
        Of the heights.

Twilight on Union Street

George Held

Swifts swirl
            in currents
        over
The Whalers' Church
                    where
once

                        d
                    e
                r
            a
            o
    a steeple s
        ro
Aerial ac
                bats
dart
    with
                incr
    edible
            speed
                    too
fast
for my eye
            to
fasten
    on

St. Andrew's Church, Division Street

The race

            goes

                    to

the

                    t

                            s

        swi

            f

Southfork

Scott Chaskey

These reeds I see are full of tears:
  summer rain simplified by grass,
    the pathway of water interrupted by matter.

As it falls the blue heron steps
  through grains of a great web.
    Sand, reeds, rain,

translucent as years,
  water tangible as tears
    on grasses by the salt pond.

Called globes, each orb of rain
  touched by grass, fluid in rest,
    reflects reeds, wings, the surface glitter of summer,
clarity of dwelling in one body.

Long Island

Megan Chaskey

Here, needles shine,
    fray from each crook
        of pine limb,
    here shadows climb
      the afternoon.

His eyes
    follow his own hands
  as they smooth the child's
      copper resistance
        from her face,

skein by skein:
he talks of the music in things.

His pockets are hemmed with
tiny carrot seeds,
that shift against
the pencil,
the pipe stem,
silver coins,
folds of paper.

The music that has gone
underground
comes up now
in the seeded lines.

Farmer,
father in the quintet house,
his rhythm stays
a delight
in the deep
resonance of soil.

Spring, Sag Harbor

Megan Chaskey

The first Japanese Maple leaves
hang folded wings
like tiny scarlet bats
clinging to
the wine blossoms
in this May northerly.
Each day color broadens
out from the floral breath
at the tips
of twigs.
At heart
in each wind-banked
corner drift
of last year's
warm brown oak leaves,
the new green sharpens itself
up each grass blade
toward the light.

When I leave
this place I love,
how will the green, daily,
unravel the tangle
of my heart?

Brush Neck Cove, Sag Harbor: Ice

Megan Chaskey

How is it that ice surfaces the whole belly
    of our tidal bay?
      not cracking like anger?
        freezes and still moves
            how water breathes?
Tide falls,
    tonight, and bay, under vellum of ice,
      plays its edges against lips of sand.
Tide rises,
    and the shallows never seal,
        never marked out in circumference
          as nations are.
Is it so simple?
    Original wholeness forgives
      itself of boundaries.
 Center is all,
      omnipresent.

The whole listening force gives audience —
    yes, frozen,
  ice is water, not fluid, still water,
      with some earth suspended,
        metal diffused in solution,
      all elements held in check —
  the moment music is
    pure change
      at the stillpoint, turning

within itself,
beyond itself

until the sister air carves the crystal edge
as thin as light
and marks the floor of sky
where buffle-heads and cormorant
walk on water.

To the Fire

Sam Holmes

The old geezer
has made a truce
with his wife.

They sleep in separate beds

He gets up early, cold,
lets out the dog
drinks coffee,
watching
TV news — to gather ammo for the day.

Now, somewhat hooked into
the wobbly world,
he zips his jacket, launching out
for Gleason's deli,
where the lights are on.

There, others like him
greet with welcome taunts.

And over second cups and thirds
their skeptic words and cynic words crackle and snap-
kindling for the fire
that warms this needed hearth.

Barcelona Neck

Monica Enders

Have you been back to that place
near Northwest Creek
the small hollow we nestled in
resting on fallen leaves
hummocks of moss
spring sun warming bones
stiffened from the throes of winter.

Remember how we tilted our faces
up to the sun, nibbled on
boiled eggs and bread
sipping our tea
the old lilacs heavy with bloom
ready to release their perfume
into the arms of May.

Have you revisited
our impressions
left in the sand napping
where the car's rusted undercarriage
nicked your skin and drew
drops of warm blood
into the loaming earth.

I think of how you rejoiced:
Ah Spring! It is all too much
everything happening at once!

And the alewives were running
in creeks fed by the bay
their silver-white bellies
scudding through the shallows.

Have you looked for that land
set upon by suns and moons
the passing of seasons.
You needn't wait for me.
I will return to that place
longing for lilacs.

from Morning, Noon and Night

Spalding Gray

… As soon as I get out on the road I start to unwind and I start thinking. "Wow, why has it taken me so long to get out of there?" Now I'm riding past the historic cemetery on my left, to turn right on Jermain Avenue and ride by the other, not quite so historic cemetery, Oakland Cemetery. How I love these cemeteries. They are such great negative spaces and it's nice to be almost sure that the greedy contractors can't develop there. Now I am riding past the duck pond on my right and headed for the intersection of Main Street and Brick Kiln Road. I ride straight through the traffic light, which takes me very quickly out of the historic village of Sag Harbor and into a hodgepodge of crazy, mixed-up architecture. I pass the fire station on my right, which gives me a clear view of my first American flag of the day, which tells me in its colorful way that we have a healthy northwest wind (I remember the prevailing wind that brings our daily radioactive dose over from the Millstone Reactor) blowing at about fifteen knots. So that means as I turn right on Noyac Road I will be heading into the wind and will have to push a little harder. I like that. I like having to do that because riding harder is both waking me up and focusing me in a good way as I ride with my own self-imposed invisible blinders on. I am being careful not to look at or take in too much of this geography of nowhere, or anywhere. It could be anywhere in central Long Island. It could be Huntington, Amityville, or Syosset. It's all an homogeny of random, chaotic styles. There are row houses, ranch houses,

split-levels with fake brass carriage lamps mounted by the door. Beach bun-galows, one two-day-old prefab I'd not noticed before. And then there are the great, three-million-dollar baronic trophy homes with four oversized faux-Provence château-style chimneys and a four-car garage, just plunked down there in the middle of an unlandscaped potato field. These houses are used only three months of the year. I also see vinyl-sided colonial-style houses with oversized large-load white plastic shrinkwrapped power boats looking like giant Clorox bottles perched on undersized trailers in the yard. I see Boston whalers and rusting Buicks for sale, jeeps for sale, night crawlers, firewood, pick-your-own-pumpkins-here, hot rods, speedboats, lobster pots, live bait and snails. Oh, the stupefying clutter of it all.

Then, all of a sudden, "POW!" I'm out and riding along the water and shock-a-roo! It's a million-dollar view! It's all a glorious out-of-season Carib-bean blue! Now that northwest wind is behind me and driving me on as my head opens up over the bay. Seagulls hover and soar and that old familiar smell of autumn mixed with brine enters and fills me. I am riding fast and smooth now with the brilliant energizing bay on my left, then out of the

Long Beach parking lot, I ride onto Route 114. And coming in for my final run as I pass the North Haven Settlement sign which reads "Settled in 1664," I turn right at the blinking light, I turn right and head for my final run to the little bridge that goes over the estuary to Sag Harbor Cove and links North Haven to the village of Sag Harbor. As I ride now I see roadkill. Dead squirrels smashed on the road. And I smell the reek of a dead deer on the side. I spy the gaping torn anus where the first little critters have gnawed their hungry way in. Then I see that angering pile of discarded 7-Eleven coffee cups that keeps growing in the same place every day, because the same workers just happen to finish their coffee at that spot as they turn in to build yet another giant trophy home.

Then suddenly I feel that tingle in my crotch. I realize my whole crotch has gone to sleep. I've lost all the feeling in my groin, so I jump off my bike and walk it for a while. As I walk, I enjoy the feeling of the blood rushing back in.

Now for the final homestretch I ride up onto the bridge that spans the channel of water that separates Sag Harbor from North Haven. When I get to the center of the bridge I stop. There in the middle of the bridge I am up high enough to have my first partial overview of the town. Just to my left I see a sweet little cove that may soon be destroyed by Tommy Mottola, the president of Sony Music, who is trying to build a two-hundred-foot-long private jet-ski dock. I try to block this great giant penis party dock out of my mind and enjoy what's left of the pristine cove for what it is now. Beyond this cove I see the long wharf, where the whaling ships used to come in. I see another American flag blowing maybe twenty knots now and I see the harbor with its elegant sailboats. Then I see the breakwater and the bay beyond. In the distance, I see the nature conservancy on Shelter Island. It's so lovely to see such undeveloped land all stretching out in that autumnal, purplish rusty hue.

To my right I see what looks like a sort of medieval wall of a motel, condos, two professional buildings, and three restaurants, all surrounding the

Methodist Church, Madison Street

village, which peaks up behind them like a pop-up card with old colonial brick-and-clapboard Victorians, and all its churches. Then, in its ludicrous way, as if put there to save the town from becoming a piece of generic calendar art, there sits a big blue one-hundred-foot-high natural-gas ball. It looks like a giant pool ball that has just rolled into town and come to rest.

I love this little overview and I think, as I stand on that bridge, I wish the town had a little hill I could climb up and look back down from. I would love to climb up a hill just to get that godly distance on it all, just to have that overview. Once, I did have a God's-eye overview, when I was flying back from London with my family in a giant 747. We flew right over Sag Harbor in the daylight and we all looked down at the old Whalers' Church, at our house and the long wharf. It was a true God's-eye view and all of Sag Harbor looked like a Norman Rockwell Monopoly town. It was all just nestled there with its off-season population of 2,009, about the size of the population of an average New York City subway at rush hour.

I remember the first time I rode over this bridge on my new bike just after moving here. I remember the feeling of what I can only call a complicated present. By that I mean where I am present and in the past at the same time. It was because the place was so familiar in a very old sense and yet, at the same time, new. I felt as though I'd come home to Rhode Island without quite having to go there. Rhode Island is, as the gull flies, only about thirty miles northeast. Standing there on that bridge for the first time, I felt as if I had returned to the place that I started from and was about to know it for the first time. Circles are, I think, so important to me, or to us. Circles are important because we only live once. Repeating, or coming around full circle, gives us the feeling of rebirth, of living again. The seasons do that as well. These circles bend the relentless, unmarked horizontal march of time. They take us away and they bring us back. So, after thirty years of self-imposed exile from my land of islands and sea, I came full circle, and as I stood there on that bridge the idea occurs to me that if I wrapped my arms around myself, and just stood there so very, very still, I would feel that I had at last come home. I felt that if I stood very still I would finally feel a sense of belonging. I would feel connected to this place, this single place on Earth.

I stood there for the longest time, just waiting. I stood and I waited. I stood, but I never felt the stillness I was longing for. All I felt was motion all around and under me. Like the water flowing under that very bridge. The stillness never came, but what did come was the realization that there is no place where we can arrive. It is all transiency, impermanence, and change. When I realized this, I felt the only appropriate thing to do was be in motion, so I got on my bike and I rode.

Tony's Coffee Shop, Sag Harbor Turnpike

Anniversary Song

Anthony Brandt

I was walking home along the waterfront the other day, stopped to look at the harbor, which was empty and still, one lonely canvasback adrift on the flat surface, shiny gray in the late winter light, and suddenly it occurred to me that this month, March, is the twenty-fifth anniversary of my moving to Sag Harbor.

I had been living in an apartment in Ossining by myself, having been dumped by my girlfriend, who told me that I would never make enough money to keep her in the style to which she was accustomed. She subsequently married a banker. Then early in February I met Lorraine, who was already living here and would become my wife with a speed that amazed us both. By the end of the month we had rented a house across the street from Jim Federico's market, which is now Espresso. Three years later we moved to High Street. Two years after that we bought the house we were renting there.

Twenty five years. In February 1981 Sag Harbor had twenty-three bars. We counted them one night on a bar tour. We decided to get married in Murph's, and no, we weren't drunk. We were drinking Rolling Rock and I'm not sure it's possible to get drunk on Rolling Rock. Denizens of Murph's may know better.

Murph's is still there; so is the Corner Bar. But the Black Buoy, known for its bar fights, is gone. Rose Black sold the place a long time ago. What is now Spinnaker's was the Sandbar, and not the same kind of place at all. One

night I watched a guy breakdancing in the back, where the pool table was. He was really good. He could spin on his back on the floor. The Sandbar was kind of wild. And fun. Just before I got married, a woman friend sidled up to me and said, "If it doesn't work out, let me know."

Lorraine was also a really good dancer. I was known for my singing voice. One sings, the other dances. At a party shortly after moving here I got down on my knees at a friend's house and belted out "Ol' Man River." I am, or used to be, a basso profundo. We gave parties, went to parties all the time. To Ted Conklin's alarm a group of us serenaded the diners at the American Hotel one Friday night. "Some Enchanted Evening" was the song. Ted tossed us some pennies, then he tossed us out.

I felt right away, within weeks, days, hours of moving here, that I had come home.

Maybe, as well as soul mates, we have soul places.

But I also knew right away that I could never know Sag Harbor the way a native knows it. I wasn't born here, didn't go to Pierson, didn't have relatives up or down the block. When we helped George Butts become mayor in

1985 he had a list of all the voters, and Fred Butts and George and George Simonson and Jim Federico could look at that list and know just how people were going to vote. One guy had been feuding with his cousin most of his life and his cousin was a friend of Fred Runco's or Dave Lee's, so he would vote one way; somebody else had a beef with John Harrington, the police chief then, so he would vote another; or there would be some other reason that only a native with a long memory could really understand.

Forgive me, I've told that story before. But it's central to my point. Memory is the thing. Nothing was written down. People *knew* who was who, what was what, how the place worked. They'd always known. Communities are like this, founded on gossip. When the gossip goes away, so does the community.

But if I didn't belong here, I didn't *not* belong here, either. America is remarkably fluid when it comes to the question of belonging. In Europe nobody moves; the mobility rates are so low it hinders the economy. Romans don't want to leave Rome; Liverpudlians stay in Liverpool, ugly as it is, no matter what. People born in Ghent spend their lives in Ghent, even if the best jobs are in Brussels.

In America it's quite different. The mobility rate is high, something like nineteen percent a year. People just don't stay put. And the more attractive a place is, the more people move into and out of it. You can see it on Main Street, Captain's Row. I think five houses are for sale on Main Street right now. Maybe six. The people who can afford them will buy them, have their Sag Harbor year or two because a Sag Harbor year has become so fashionable among the rich, and then they sell out. At a profit, of course. If they had the patience to get to know the place they might stay longer, but they mostly don't. For most it turns out not to be what they expected. The locals don't give a damn who they are. Plumbers, carpenters, masons don't call back. The community will fight you tooth and nail if you want to build big and ugly to satisfy your ambition. That's hard on the ego.

No, it's definitely not what they expected. It has changed enormously in the last twenty-five years, gone upscale, lost its working-class edge, become unaffordable for its native sons and daughters. The bars are almost sedate.

But I still see faces on the streets and in the stores that I first saw in 1981, people will form a committee in a New York minute if something or somebody threatens an historic building, and we all still vote unpredictably in local elections and local issues still get us mad. The place is lively. Something is always happening. Most nights the streets of East Hampton village are empty. Here, Main Street is lined with cars.

I don't have to rehearse all of Sag Harbor's virtues — the movie theater, the five-and-dime, the Bay Street Theatre, the Hotel, the shops — none of them so far an Eddie Bauer or Ann Taylor or a Starbucks. Those of us who dig in know them well. It has enough foreigners to qualify as cosmopolitan, it has mixed marriages, it has a satisfying number of bookstores. It is beautiful. It has water, boats, it has Anselm Morpurgo.

You can make a place a home, even if it's not your home. This is not my home. I belong in a New Jersey suburb where many of my family still live. But I've never lived anywhere as long as I've lived here, and I couldn't be happier about it. So thank you, Sag Harbor, for being you. Twenty-five years. They have been without question the best of my life.

Stalking Sag Harbor 1991

Pat Sweeney

I

Under Sag spires of United Methodist
St. Andrews Christ Church and absent omnipresent
Egyptian revival Old Whalers First Presbyterian
a southwest breeze blows in balmy
and spurs our Spring's imaginings to
near frenzied pitch   we stalk
we navigate the sidewalk
in search of coffee and the times
as narcissi bud and bob and burst at one another
over the greening lawns and the song-strung
throats of toads come up from the mud

And yet is there any Hell like the one here
on Earth created between thee and me
and the cats   yowling it into
existence under our windows thrown open to the breeze
while planes drop-load it in tonnage over Persia
the sun choked in a black sky

Mary Delmonico King and friends

Rains will maim Bhopal again in the coming season
and yet again we will fall and fall
in love on Spring days

and look for the bellies of women
to bear into existence the small ones
for whom and on whom we pin all hell and hopefulness
in this simple watery blue–green orb
gliding through the universe caressed
by cloud-cover   an aureole of atmosphere
and the radiance of star-light   moon-light
sun-light

II

The ivied wall of the church yard
seven feet tall
stays a hill swollen with dead seafarers
to walk its hundred meter length is to confront
the unceasing singularity of our steps
the sound tossed between the stone wall
and white clapboard of the church
the preservation of order
and the bracketed phrases of village life
a sacred book of ordinances
maps of tidy cottages and quadrilateral lots

Lead on to the harbor where one longs
to eat the mollusks from their pristine fans
and dip into a silvery school of fish for supper
the breeze from Hatteras
calling us to cancel our preoccupations
come   it says   come next to the water
the radiant bay   the black lake   the heaving Atlantic
the biding river or the creek
sit upon the shore   the bridge   the sandy bank
remain until the eyes, awash and hallucinatory
view the water leaping over
the lip of the horizon or shivering in the trees
until the being of you
the alive
cracks free the somnambulant husk
unfurls the violet bunting

Oakland Cemetery, Sag Harbor

Margaret B. Brehmer

Vandalism, perhaps.
And perhaps not.

I have stood alone and quiet
in the filtered sunlight
beneath the old trees,
listening to the sighing wind
and the chattering of birds,
and heard a gentle thud.
A gravestone just topples over
and lies there cracked
on the stubble of grass.

After nearly 200 years,
"Abigail, beloved wife of Josiah"
steps out of line and falls over
beside her upright peers —
all those others, standing straight and stoic,
quiet and resigned, in their sandstone rows.

"Mary, beloved wife of Josiah…"
who preceded Abigail in life and in death.
"Jane, infant daughter, much mourned…"
"William, son of Abigail and Josiah,
lost at sea in the 18th year of his life."

What restless yearning has disturbed
the upright obedience of this stone?
What longing — to see yet one more
sunrise on the bay? One more look
for the ship that has never returned?
To hear the men boasting and laughing
as they mend their nets?
Or see the children dance
once again down to the wharf?

An afterthought perhaps,
one final point to make
in the women's call
for justice at Sunday meeting?

After all those years,
what unfinished dreaming
now demands another moment of life?

from The Whaler's Gift

Val Schaffner

Halloween is a night of festivity and enigma in old Sag Harbor, when it is apropos to wonder, at certain moments, whose children were those, rapping and giggling by the door, but gone when we opened it; who was that we saw in the mirror at the candlelit masquerade party, garbed in black from head to toe, but gone when we turned; who in the group by the fire murmured a cryptic something in our ears, in a voice not that of the masked woman beside us, whom we knew; why did the wine glass tip on the table, when no one had touched it; and what was that knocking in the attic, after the guests went home?

Later the ghosts of the place drifted off to their own parties, in certain houses hallowed by tradition for that purpose, but their chatter was more subdued than usual, this year, and its topic not cheerful.

Where, they sighed, as they sipped ancient brandies and bootleg gin, will our Christmas party be, this year?

Where will our Halloween parties be, next year?

It is the beginning of the end, they said.

Meanwhile the twins and some half dozen of their friends zipped from one haunt to another in search of their bearded companion. They found him atop the tower of the Isaiah Mistral house, by the Oakland Cemetery, where a party of solemn ghosts had risen to watch the progression of Aquarius, Pisces, and Cetus across the southern sky.

173

You promised, the twins nagged.

Very well, he replied, tapping the ash from his ancient pipe.

Once upon a time, he began, there lived in Sag Harbor two sisters, whose names were Felicity and Emily Bedford. Felicity, the elder, a tall, dark-haired young woman given to swiftly changing moods of exuberance and melancholy, was courted by a young whaler, first mate on the *Belinda*, whose captain was old Tobias Hand.

This young whaler was an orphan, born in mysterious circumstances. Some say he was brought to this village by the servants of a fine lady from New York, who left him on the steps of the Presbyterian manse with a purse of gold. Be that as it may, he was raised for a time by the minister and was thereafter adopted by Juliet Porter, the widowed sister of Captain Mortimer. He grew into a fine, tall lad, with a mane of black hair and flashing dark eyes, towards whom all bonnets turned when he appeared for service in the Presbyterian Church.

Perhaps the manner of his origin and upbringing disposed him to a solitary, brooding temper. So it often seemed, when he would wander alone in the fields at night, studying the heavens, and surpassed all his classmates in the grim tenacity with which he mastered the arts of mathematics and navigation. Yet at other times he exulted in sportive and sociable pursuits, charming all his contemporaries, not least of them his neighbor Felicity.

By their sameness of temperament it appeared the young couple were well matched, as indeed they were, except for a touch of jealousy that flawed both their characters, so that each was ever intent upon the other, lest some rival appear.

So it happened that, on returning from his first sea voyage aboard the *Belinda*, and making straightaway for the Bedford place on Madison Street, the young whaler was not pleased to find his beloved, and her younger sister Emily, at tea with a handsome youth by the name of Robert Mortimer, who was telling them such stories that they quaked in fits of laughter. It was with

a dour face indeed that the returning seaman shook the hand of this unexpected guest, his adoptive cousin, and partook of a proffered scone.

Now the whole reason for the presence of this young Robert, the son of
Captain Mortimer, was the affection he harbored for the fair Emily, who was
as unalike her sister in temper as the fickle sea and a sheltered bay. Yet he
thought himself constrained, from politeness, to bestow his eloquence
equally upon both sisters, when he visited them together; while Felicity, it
must be said, sometimes took pleasure in pricking the heart of her dark
swain, by affecting to hold him in no higher esteem than Robert. When at
Christmas Robert presented each sister with a little ivory cat, though he had
carved Emily's with love and Felicity's with haste, the raven-haired whaler
fairly choked with jealousy.

His discomfiture grew throughout the winter. Though Felicity most often paid
him the highest marks of affection, and though he could demonstrate no palpable
cause for envy, yet he could not rid himself of this distress. It did not strike him
that Emily was the real object of his cousin's attentions, perhaps because she was at
that time only 16, and outwardly deferred to her sister in everything.

So it was with mingled reassurance and ire that the young whaler learned, as he prepared for his second expedition aboard the *Belinda*, that Robert was to be with him among the crew. The voyage proceeded without event until, off the coast of California, Robert harpooned a fearsome sperm whale, reckoned to be the largest of its kind ever taken by a ship out of Sag Harbor.

Rather than exult at this feat, Robert seemed suddenly to grieve, calling the whale the noblest of God's creatures, and himself a man in the wrong and most ignoble profession. Be that as it may, he took a piece of bone from the slain leviathan and commenced to carve from it a wonderfully intricate box, with forms of frolicking whales around the edges and lid.

The brooding first mate, inwardly reasoning that his cousin's compunctions had justice, but himself more eager for whale oil and wealth, with which to dazzle Felicity, grew uneasy when he saw the care that was lavished, hour upon hour, in carving the splendid box.

What will you keep in that box? he asked one day.

Nothing, Robert replied.

What are you polishing within it?

Oh, a mirror, said Robert. There is a mirror on its bottom.

Then it seemed to the dark whaler that Robert was carving the box as a gift for Felicity, that she might regard herself in its depth, and thereby be charmed by its donor; or else that he might enclose some bright jewel, and win her that way. Robert himself was oblivious to these suspicions; so intent was he on his marvelous carvings, he never perceived his cousin's dour gaze upon him.

The grim one's fears grew apace as the *Belinda* journeyed across the Pacific. If at times he recalled that it was he and not Robert whom Felicity had favored with an ardent kiss, before the cousins boarded the ship at Long Wharf, at others he would brood exquisitely upon the last season he had spent at sea, and Robert on shore, and wonder what might have come to pass there, that fiery summer, between him and her.

Yes, said the lean ghost, looking around at his listeners with a twinkle in his dark eyes, 'twas torment to be alive, but bliss also. I miss it still, sometimes, even in these exalted starry nights of our haunting.

In the second day of a tempest off the islands of Japan (the ghost resumed), the melancholy first mate, spelling the exhausted captain at the wheel as mountainous waves crashed upon the deck and swept away the long boats and cannon, even savored the thought of letting the ship founder, and so putting an end both to his anxiety and to Robert. He steered the *Belinda* safely through anyhow, shrinking from plain murder as from suicide, but a dark plot, as the crew sighted land soon after, took form in his mind.

At that time the inhabitants of Japan were by no means kindly disposed toward foreigners, as Captain Hand knew from a previous voyage, when they had promised to lock him in a menagerie, if he did not hasten to quit their vicinity. He also recalled, however, a certain island, called Nii, where a party could land out of sight of a village on the other side, and take on fresh water, of which the *Belinda* was now much in need.

Our dour friend offered to land there in the ship's wherry, which had weathered the storm, and requested Robert Mortimer to accompany him. That night, beneath a full moon, the two rowed ashore with as many casks as the little boat could hold — the first mate having taken care, however, that the number of these was odd.

Together they made their way up a hill to where a cool spring flowed, each with an empty cask, and down again with a full one. Stealthily, lest they arouse the nearby village, they repeated the climb until 12 filled casks were stowed in the boat and one remained.

I'll make ready to push off, whispered the grim whaler, while you fill the last cask.

When Robert had toiled unsuspectingly up the hill, his companion swiftly pushed the boat through the surf, fired his pistol in the air, and rowed with all his strength back to the *Belinda*, where he raised a great cry, that they had been assailed by fearsome Japanese with swords, who had slain Robert Mortimer.

Captain Hand, reflecting that his tempest-tossed crew was in poor condition for battle, that with Robert slain there would be no point in it, and that a menagerie had little to recommend itself as a place for his retirement, gave orders to set sail from the island with all speed.

The remainder of their voyage, the *Belinda* having stopped at Shanghai for provisions and repairs, was singularly fortunate, her crew bringing home such a quantity of oil as to delight her owners, among them her captain, who retired forthwith upon North Haven.

In the meantime, however, the melancholy first mate stole from Robert Mortimer's berth the charming box of whalebone. Shutting himself with it in his cabin, he moodily lifted its lid and peered inside.

I know not for certain (said the ghost) what the dark whaler saw within, only that it was some abominable thing; for ever after he carried with him a look of horror, and nightly could not forbear but to look again in the box, as if in prayer that this thing had now gone.

Nor can I affirm by what cause he saw it there; whether from the evil of the deed upon which he acquired it, or some miraculous trick of the craftsman's art, or some potency of the fearsome sperm whale from whose bone it was wrought, or all of these together, or none, can only be guessed at.

In any event, he said not a word, and varied not his ill humor, when he learned soon after his return to Sag Harbor of the death of Byron Mortimer; of his own fortune, for as the adopted son of the captain's late sister, now thought to be his only survivor, he inherited all the family wealth; and of the vanishing of Emily Bedford, who was thought to have drowned in Gardiner's Bay.

It was with a lackluster air that, in the Presbyterian Church, the dark-clad whaler wed Felicity Bedford, and with her took residence in the grand house that the late Captain Mortimer had recently completed.

Felicity could not but wonder why her husband, who before his first voyage had sparkled sometimes with high spirits, and before his second, though stricken with jealously had yet been goaded by it to outperform his supposed rival in wit and ardor, now seemed only to grieve, making of their marriage a funeral.

Reflecting on these coincidences, poor Felicity jumped to the conclusion that the thing he mourned so extravagantly was none other than the loss of her sister, Emily; and, fired by this suspicion, she commenced to make of his life even more of an ordeal than it was already. She could not but note that he carried with him everywhere a white box, into which he continually peeked with an air of desolation. Presently she hit upon the idea that it must have been a gift to him from Emily, and that it must be a portrait of Emily at which he was wont to gaze within. Thereafter, every evening at dinner, she demanded of him that he should give her the box. When he would not show it, and locked it in his desk instead, her suspicion seemed to her confirmed.

During this time, whether despite his morbidity or because of it, the taciturn whaler applied himself ruthlessly to the multiplication of the fortune he had inherited from Byron Mortimer. This included to start with two whaling ships, which soon returned to port with such bounty that he was able to purchase two more, including the *Belinda*, which he renamed the *Felicity*. He also speculated in property, and built saloons and rooming houses on the outlying streets of the village, from which he drew great profits.

His fellow citizens, seeing that he regarded them with scant warmth, shunned him in turn, except for certain men of business who liked to be associated with the profits that he made; and even these men complained, among themselves, that he dealt with them in a manner that could not be called amiable. When a subscription was announced for the erection of a new and magnificent Presbyterian Church, therefore, it was with pleasant surprise that the villagers heard the promise of the grim whaler, that he would himself match, with an equal grant, any sum that was raised in Sag Harbor for the building fund.

After he had made this promise, he retired to his study in the Mortimer house, where Felicity, spying through a keyhole, watched him take out that mysterious box from his desk and gaze again within, his countenance writ with renewed melancholy. Baring her teeth like a hound, as she knelt on the Indian carpet in the hall, she resolved to have done with this irksome thing.

In the evening, when the whaler returned from the inspection of one of his barques at Long Wharf, he found the desk in his study smashed in pieces, with an ax that lay beside it on the floor, and the box gone. With a vigor he had not shown in two years, he bounded through the house and bellowed warnings to Felicity, not to look in the box.

He was too late. When he discovered her, sitting in their bed upstairs, she was gazing silently into the box and shaking her head with a sorrowful mien. Whatever it was that she saw there, it affected her as strangely as what he saw had him. Nor could he induce her thereafter to speak; through the remainder of her days she kept her silence, and only wandered about the house, shaking her head.

She is silent still, the ghost added, pointing with his piped stem across the cemetery, where a dark-haired wraith wandered, shaking her head.

Notes on Contributors

STAR BLACK is the author of five books of poems, mostly recently *Ghost-wood*, published by Melville House, 2003. Her poems are anthologized in *The Penguin Book of the Sonnet* and *110 Stories: New York Writes After September 11*. "Descent" and "Traffic" were written in Sag Harbor at the end of summer and are included in her collection, *Balefire*.

ANTHONY BRANDT grew up on the Jersey shore but prefers Long Island. He has written for various national magazines and currently edits a series of reprinted exploration classics for the National Geographic Society including *The Tragic History of the Sea*; *Thomas Jefferson Travels*; and *The Journals of Lewis and Clark*. He is also working on a book about the Northwest Passage.

MARGARET B. BREHMER taught French for years, raised three children, and was editor at a non-profit agency that promoted literacy worldwide. She and her husband Frank lived in North Haven for 30 years. They now reside at Peconic Landing in Greenport.

OLIVIA WARD BUSH-BANKS (1869–1944) was born in Sag Harbor's Eastville community though she left when very young. A life-long champion of Indian rights, she returned to Sag Harbor to attend tribal meetings. She was a teacher, playwright, and poet and worked through the WPA as a community drama director. Her poems were praised by poet Paul Laurence Dunbar. *The Collected Works of Olivia Ward Bush-Banks* was published by Oxford University Press in 1991.

MARYANN CALENDRILLE has had articles, essays, and poems appear in various publications. She is a freelance editor and writing instructor. In 1999 she and Kathryn Szoka took over Canio's Books. Over the past 20 years, she has observed Sag Harbor from five different vantage points: two village apartments, a ranch in North Haven, another near Noyac, and now a cape in Bay Point.

MEGAN CHASKEY poet, musician, and yoga teacher has lived in Sag Harbor with her husband poet, farmer Scott Chaskey, for 16 years, raising three children. Her recent volume of poems, *Voice*, pairs each poem with a black and white image by her step-father, East Hampton sculptor William King.

SCOTT CHASKEY, a poet, farmer, and educator has taught poetry for over 20 years. His most recent book of poems, *Stars are Suns*, is included in the rare books collection of the Houghton Library. Employed by the Peconic Land Trust as a steward of land, he has farmed for over 15 years at Quail Hill Farm, one of the original community-supported agriculture farms in the country. He edited *Free Concert*, the final collection of poems by his former teacher, Milton Kessler (Etruscan Press, 2004). *This Common Ground: Seasons on an Organic Farm* was published in 2005 by Viking/Penguin. He lives in Sag Harbor with his wife Megan and their three children.

MARK CIABATTARI is a novelist, essayist, and cultural historian. He has taught at various universities and colleges including Yeshiva, New York University, Baruch, Mercy, and John Jay. He has lectured on the literary history of the East End. His book *The Literal Truth: Rizzoli Dreams of Eating the Apple of Earthly Delights, Tales of Manhattan and the Hamptons* was published by Canio's Editions in 1994.

VINCE CLEMENTE is a poet–biographer whose books include *John Ciardi: Measure of the Man*. His poetry collections include *Under a Baleful Star: a Garland for Margaret Fuller; Sweeter Than Vivaldi; Paumanok Rising;* and *A Place for Lost Children* among other titles. Clemente is English Professor Emeritus, SUNY Stony Brook. The Vince Clemente Papers are now part of the Rush Rhees Library, Department of Rare Books & Collections of the Rochester University.

JAMES FENIMORE COOPER (1789–1851) visited Sag Harbor with his wife Susan A. Delancy whose relatives lived on Shelter Island. Between 1818 and

1820, Cooper owned a share in the Sag Harbor whaleship *Union* and began his novel *Precaution* while staying here. The colorful local sea captain, David Hand provided inspiration for Cooper's Natty Bumppo character from the *Leatherstocking Tales.*

LORRAINE DUSKY's most recent book is *Still Unequal: The Shameful Truth about Women and Justice in America.* It carries a blurb by Betty Friedan on the back cover. She is also the author of *Birthmark.* Published in 1979, it was the first memoir from the point of view of a woman who surrenders a child to adoption.

MONICA ENDERS has lived in Cleveland, California, and New York. After living on a sailboat, she moved to the East End 25 years ago. She's been a taxi driver, waitress, and presently works as a gardener. When she was nine, she discovered her aunt's collection of Shakespeare, fell in love with literature and has been writing ever since.

BETTY FRIEDAN: (1921–2006) At her Sag Harbor home, preeminent feminist and author of the ground-breaking *Feminine Mystique*, Betty Friedan hosted many lively summertime gatherings of family, friends and distinguished guests, writers and intellectuals among them. She is buried in Hevre Kedotia Cemetery near Sag Harbor.

SPALDING GRAY: (1941–2004) Monologist, actor and writer Spalding Gray lived with his family in Sag Harbor village and in North Haven. He was often seen riding his bicycle through town. The inscription on his gravestone at Oakland Cemetery reads: "an American original, troubled, inner-directed, and cannot type."

ELIZABETH THUNDER BIRD HAILE is an enrolled member of Shinnecock Nation, Shinnecock Reservation. She is the daughter of the late Chief Thunder Bird, ceremonial chief of Shinnecock and the late Edith Thunder Bird. She is a consultant in Native American Studies and Shinnecock History and is vice president of the Shinnecock Nation Cultural Center and Museum board of directors. In 2000 she was awarded an honorary doctorate in letters from Southampton College.

JOE HANNA wrote an award-winning humor column for *The Sag Harbor Express* for over 15 years. He has played music professionally and once toured with a bluegrass band throughout the South and West. He's had day jobs in architectural drafting, sound engineering, mechanical engineering, theatrical special effects, and cabinet making. He doesn't recall ever being bored. Hanna lived for many years in an old house in Sag Harbor village. He now lives on Shelter Island.

GEORGE HELD has spent part of the year in Sag Harbor since 1971. He has written about local plants and animals, people and places, and his experiences as a gardener. A three-time Pushcart Prize nominee, he has published eight collections of poems, including *Beyond Renewal* (2001) and *Grounded* (2005). Two more collections, *Edgedale* and *W Is for War*, will appear in 2006. The poems included here are from *Winged*, 1995.

SAM HOLMES has been a reporter, graphics researcher, and educator. For the National Park Service he organized environmental education programs for New York City school children. Besides poems, he writes articles for circus publications, and has recently completed a short novel *So Long, Big Duck*, about two boys who get into trouble during their vacation in Sag Harbor.

LANGSTON HUGHES: (1902–1967) A visitor to Eastville, Langston Hughes was a guest of the William Pickens family in the early 1950s. Langston Hughes and William Pickens were classmates at Lincoln University, the historically black college in Pennsylvania. Hughes introduced Pickens to Emily Montier Brown, then a good friend of Langston. William and Emily would later marry. Friendships forged at Lincoln continued through the years linking many residents of Eastville.

VELDA JOHNSTON: (1911–1997) The author of 34 romantic suspense novels, Velda Johnston lived in Sag Harbor. She also wrote under the name Veronica Jason. Her first published novel appeared in 1968. Her last novel was *The Underground Stream* published in 1991.

HERMAN MELVILLE: (1819–1891) We're not certain whether Melville actually visited Sag Harbor, but he certainly knew of this notorious "sin city." As Captain Ahab chased the great white whale across the oceans, many writers have been drawn to Sag Harbor in pursuit of the illusive Great American Novel. They write in the wake of Melville's *Moby Dick*.

WALTER MOSLEY: Best known as the author of the acclaimed Easy Rawlins' murder mysteries, Mosley has also published science fiction and an essay collection *What Next? A Memoir Toward World Peace*. For several summers he rented a home in Sag Harbor and has read from his work at Canio's Books.

WILLIAM MULVIHILL (1923–2004) was born on Glover Street. He wrote hundreds of essays and over a dozen novels, many set on the South Fork. One of his early novels, *The Sands of Kalahari* became a *New York Times* bestseller, won the first Putnam award and became a Paramount picture in 1965. He also wrote *The Mantrackers* (also published as *Serengeti*), *Night of the Axe*, *Sagaponack* and *Meadow Lane*, as well as the popular local history book *South Fork Place Names*. Bill was an avid environmentalist. The Anna and Daniel Mulvihill Preserve in Southampton, named for his parents, is a testament to his and his family's dedication to habitat preservation.

FRANCES HUNT PALMER: (1870–1925) Born in Sag Harbor, Frances Hunt Palmer, a daughter of Dr. Peter Roosevelt Johnson and Mary C. Hunt was one of nine children. Fanny, as she was known, became a nurse in 1892. She lectured for Women's Suffrage and volunteered for duty during World War I though since she was forty years old, she did not serve. She lived on Martha's Vineyard and devoted herself to poetry. After her death, her husband William Lincoln Palmer published a collection of her work.

CANIO PAVONE founded Canio's Books in Sag Harbor in 1980 where he hosted weekly cultural events for nearly twenty years. He received an honorary doctorate in letters from Southampton College. "Sitting for Mike" is an excerpt from his forthcoming memoir, *Call Me Canio*.

JOE PINTAURO is a novelist and playwright, author of *Cold Hands*, *Raft of the Medusa*, and a dramatization of Peter Matthiessen's *Men's Lives* among other works. He divides his time between Sag Harbor and Key West.

ALLEN PLANZ is author of *Dune Heath*, published by Canio's Editions in 1997. He is a former poetry editor at *The Nation*. He has taught college English at several universities, and has written for *The East Hampton Star*. Planz is also a licensed captain and a Tae Kwan Do black belt.

ARTHUR PRAGER has written for the *Saturday Review*, *American Heritage*, and *The New York Times Magazine*. He is the author of *Rascals at Large* and the *Mahogany Tree*. He was one of four writers who created the Disney Channel series *Mouseterpiece Theatre*, nominated for a Cable–ACE award.

PAUL RUFFINS is a writer living in Washington, D.C. with his wife Fath, and two children, Joy and Robert. He is a former editor of the NAACP's *Crisis* magazine. One of the greatest kicks of his life was coming down to Ninevah beach one day, and meeting a long-time neighbor who had made about a dozen copies of "Soul of Summer" to give away to her friends.

VAL SCHAFFNER is author of *The Algonquin Cat* and *Lost in Cyberspace: Essays and Far-Fetched Tales*. His collection of short stories set in Sag Harbor, *The Astronomer's House*, was published by Canio's Editions in 2003.

WILFRID SHEED, drama critic, essayist, and novelist, is author of numerous works of fiction and non-fiction including *Transatlantic Blues; Boys of Winter; Baseball and Lesser Sports; Essays in Disguise; In Love with Daylight;* and *Frank and Maisie* to name a few.

JOHN STEINBECK: (1902–1968) The Nobel Laureate lived in Sag Harbor from 1955 until his death in New York. He joked and drank and fished with the locals who were careful to protect his privacy. A bronze bust of Steinbeck now stands in the Jermain Library. Remembrances of the writer are included in the documentary *John Steinbeck: Sag Harbor Years* by filmmaker Tom Browngardt.

TERENCE M. SULLIVAN, a practitioner of the Bardic tradition of Ireland, sings a capella in Irish and English and writes verse inspired by the natural beauty of Sag Harbor's coves and shores. His poems have appeared in *The Blue Unicorn*, *The Long Island Quarterly* and *The Seventh Quarry*, in Swansea, Wales.

PAT SWEENEY came to Sag Harbor on a visit 25 years ago and never left. The charm of the village and its people, the nearness of the bay and ocean, the water-saturated light and expansive horizons all spoke deeply to her. She raised two children here and continues to write poems to Sag Harbor "as if we were lovers." In 1994, her collection, *A Thousand Times* was published by Canio's Editions.

KATHRYN SZOKA is best known for her Vanishing Landscapes™ series which documents the East End of Long Island's fading farmland. Other documentary subjects include organic community farming at Quail Hill in Amagansett, and caring for elderly parents — documenting her father's last year. She is co-owner of Canio's Books. Her photographs are available at Canio's Books and at Robin Rice Gallery in New York City. She has lived in Sag Harbor since 1988.

MIRIAM UNGERER's food column "Long Island Larder" first appeared in *The East Hampton Star* in August 1969 when she had just published *The Too Hot to Cook Book*. "Long Island Larder" became a regular feature in May 1980 once she and husband Wilfrid Sheed took up full-time residence in Sag Harbor. The column continued through December 2005. Miriam Ungerer is the author of *Good Cheap Food; Come Into My Parlor; Country Food: a Seasonal Journal;* and *Summertime Food*. Ms. Ungerer praises Sagaponack soil for giving our local tomatoes their uniquely "sweet and sharp" flavor.

R. B. WEBER: (1929–2004) A longtime professor of English at Southampton College, R. B. Weber published several volumes of poetry including *The Fishing-Print Poems, Poems from the Xenia Hotel*, and *Laurie's Songs*. Between 1969 and 1976, he lived with his family in a Greek Revival house built by a ship's captain on the corner of Rogers and Henry Street. During summers he took his daughters to Long Beach at sunset to swim. He enjoyed walking around the old cemeteries, especially the Old Burying Ground at the Whalers' Church.

CAROL WILLIAMS is the author of *Bringing A Garden to Life*. A writer with some training and experience in architecture, she frequently writes about landscapes, built and un-built. She was born in England, made the map of Sag Harbor in 1972, and has lived here since 1974.

Sources and Dates

Star Black. "Descent" and "Traffic," *Balefire*. 2001.

Anthony Brandt. "Anniversary Song," *Sag Harbor Express*. 2006.

Olivia Ward Bush-Banks. "Morning on Shinnecock" and "Drifting," *Original Poems*. 1899.

Margaret B. Brehmer. "Oakland Cemetery, Sag Harbor," *Autumn: an Anthology of Long Island Poetry*. 1994.

Megan Chaskey. "Long Island," "Spring, Sag Harbor" and "Brush Neck Cove, Sag Harbor: Ice." 1992.

Scott Chaskey. "Southfork." 2000.

Mark Ciabattari. "Movie Project in Development at the American Hotel at 2 a.m.," *The Literal Truth*. Canio's Editions, 1994.

Vince Clemente. "Algonquin Morning Song," "Peninsula," and "Cricket at a Poetry Reading." 2004.

Monica Enders. "Barcelona Neck." 2004.

James Fenimore Cooper. *Sea Lions*. 1820.

Lorraine Dusky. "Thank You, Ms. Betty Friedan," *Sag Harbor Express*. 2006.

Betty Friedan. *Life So Far: a Memoir*. Simon & Schuster. 2000.

Spalding Gray. *Morning Noon & Night*. Farrar, Straus, and Giroux. 1999.

Joe Hanna. "White Rabbit," *Sag Harbor Express*. 2005.

George Held. "Osprey" and "Twilight on Union Street," *Winged Poems*. 1995.

Sam Holmes. "To the Fire." 1995.

Langston Hughes. "Sea Charm," "Water-Front Streets," "Port Town," "Death of an Old Seaman" (1921–1930); Lincoln University: 1954" (1950–60), *The Collected Poems of Langston Hughes* 1994.

Velda Johnston. *The Underground Stream.* St. Martin's Press, 1991.

Herman Melville. *Moby Dick.* 1851.

Walter Mosley. *The Man In My Basement.* Little, Brown. 2004.

William Mulvihill. "The Way We Were," *Sag Harbor Express.* 2002.

Frances Hunt Palmer. "My Dear Long Island Home." 1925.

Canio Pavone. "Sitting for Mike," *Call Me Canio.* Forthcoming.

Joe Pintauro. "Algren in Exile," *Chicago Magazine.* 1988.

Alan Planz. "My Village Under a Northeaster" (1974), *Dune Heath,* Canio's Editions. 1997.

Arthur Prager. "A Wonderful Place to Write," *Sag Harbor Express.* 2006.

Paul Ruffins. "The Soul of Summer," *Ambassador.* 1998.

Val Schaffner. "Whaler's Gift," *The Astronomer's House.* Canio's Editions. 2002.

Wilfrid Sheed. "Sag Harbor: an American Beauty," *Architectural Digest.* 1990.

John Steinbeck. "My War With the Ospreys," *Holiday.* 1957.

Terence M. Sullivan. "4:30 a.m. Noyac Bay" and "Fullish Moon Lighting." 1998.

Pat Sweeney. "Stalking Sag Harbor 1991," *A Thousand Times and Other Poems.* Canio's Editions. 1994.

Miriam Ungerer. "Reveling in Tomatoes," *East Hampton Star.* 2005.

R. B. Weber. "August dusk: Sag Harbor." *Poems from the Xenia Hotel.* Street Press. 1979.

Carol Williams. "Mapping Sag Harbor." 2006.

Made in the USA
Columbia, SC
27 July 2018